D1085525

Warning!

Violence and the Supernatural

The fictional worlds of Palladium Books® are violent, deadly and filled with supernatural monsters. Other-dimensional beings, often referred to as "demons," torment, stalk and prey on humans. Other alien life forms, monsters, gods and demigods, as well as magic, insanity, and war are all elements in these books.

Some parents may find the violence, magic and supernatural elements of the games inappropriate for young readers/players. We suggest parental discretion.

Please note that none of us at Palladium Books® condone or encourage the occult, the practice of magic, the use of drugs, or violence.

The Rifter® Number 79
Your Guide to the Palladium Megaverse®!

Dedication – To the gamers who fuel our passion and our industry. Keep those imaginations burning and game on.

– Kevin Siembieda, 2017

First Printing – December, 2017

Palladium Books® Presents:

THE RIFTER® #79

BRANDT -97

Sourcebook and Guide to the Palladium Megaverse®

Coordinator & Editor in Chief: **Wayne Smith**

Editor: **Alex Marciniszyn**

Contributing Writers:
 David Collins
 Hendrik Härterich
 Mark Oberle
 Matt Reed
 Julius Rosenstein
 Kevin Siembieda

Proofreader: **Julius Rosenstein**

Cover Illustration: **Nicholas Bradshaw**

Interior Artists:
 Robert Atkins
 Nicholas Bradshaw
 Michael Mumah

Cover Logo Design: **Steve Edwards**

Credits Page Logo: **Niklas Brandt**

Typesetting & Layout: **Wayne Smith**

Art Direction: **Kevin Siembieda**

Based on the RPG rules, characters,
concepts and Megaverse® created by **Kevin Siembieda**.

Special Thanks to David, Hendrik, Mark, Matt, Julius and all our contributing writers and artists this issue, and to the hardworking Palladium staff. Our apologies to anybody who may have gotten accidentally left out or their name misspelled.

– *Kevin Siembieda, 2017*

Contents – The Rifter® #79 – 2017

Page 6 – Art

We thought you might enjoy seeing a sneak peek of the work-in-progress illustration that depicts Sovietski forces fighting invading Brodkil somewhere in Russia. It is art appearing in **Rifts® Sovietski**. The finished illustration will be inked. This book rocks.

Art by *Robert Atkins*.

Page 7 – From the Desk of Kevin Siembieda

Publisher Kevin Siembieda talks about upcoming products, Palladium's Christmas Surprise Package offer, the Palladium Open House which is only four months away (April 19-22, 2018), and the holidays. We hope your holidays are full of warmth and joy.

Page 8 – Palladium News

Publisher Kevin Siembieda offers up the latest goings-on at the Palladium home front. Processing Christmas orders and getting the next four books to the printer is what's filling our days, but there are other things happening. We are most excited about the upcoming **Palladium Open House** next April, where we hope to see record attendance.

Page 9 – Coming Attractions

Gamers have been enjoying the **Rifts® Secrets of the Atlanteans™ Dimension Book** and the **Nightbane® Dark Designs sourcebook** while we busy ourselves getting this issue of **The Rifter®** into your hands and several other titles. Like what? By the time you read this, **Rifts® Sovietski™** will be at the printer and we should be deep into work on the **Rifts® Bestiary of North America, Vol. One and Two** (the text has been collated, updates are being done, some new beasts to be added). After that comes the **Dead Reign® sourcebook: In the Face of Death**, **Rifts® The Disavowed, CS Arsenal** and other titles. Read all about them all in the coming attractions.

Page 16 – Christmas Surprise Package™
– Offer extended for a very short time

It is the deal of the holidays: 4-5 titles for what other companies charge for one core rule book. Christmas is over, but we almost always extend the Surprise Package offer a few weeks after for those of you who missed it the first time, so you can still get one. But you need to act fast. Get all the details here. Thanks for the support and may the New Year be good to you. Game on!

Page 20 – 2018 Palladium Open House

This is a gaming event you don't want to miss! **The Palladium Open House (POH)** is an epic three days of gaming (4 for those who attend VIP Thursday), in which you get to meet 30-40 Palladium personalities, game with some of them (yeah, the people who make the books you love!), get books signed, and have the time of your life. And it all takes place at the Palladium warehouse. We hope to see many of you at the POH this upcoming spring (April 19-22, 2018). Get all the details about this fun and unique experience and order your tickets today!

Page 22 – Gaming Through History
– Optional Rules for ALL Palladium Games

Hendrik Härterich presents a wonderful set of guidelines, rules and ideas for using modern characters from just about any game, whether present day or the future, and putting them into settings from Earth's past. Characters and monsters from modern horror settings like **Beyond the Supernatural** and **Nightbane®** are particularly ideal and easy to transplant into different eras of history.

Create adventures that are, in effect, parts of our unknown history. The heroic deeds of your characters – demon hunters, sorcerers, psychics, Nightbane and even superhumans – covered up and history rewritten to protect governments and the influential as well as the innocent. That's why there are no records of the vampire invasion of Boston, June, 1775; what really happened in Salem involving witches; maybe they never caught *Jack the Ripper* because there was no such person – it was really a demon or cult or Nightlord (or Nightbane) responsible, and so on.

Do not sell history short. There are epic events, battles and mysteries throughout history that would make amazing RPG campaigns. And plenty of events and heroes we know nothing about, lost in the annals of history. (Or maybe it's not the past at all, but a parallel Earth dimension that seems like past eras of Earth history.)

Epic adventures are possible, and Hendrik shows you the way to get there. He offers some fun adventure ideas for the swashbuckling era too. We loved this article and think you will be excited by the ideas it has to offer. Game on!

Artwork by *Michael Mumah*.

The Theme for this Issue

The theme for **The Rifter®** #79 is adventures and imagination unleashed, as this issue presents new and alternative ideas and carries you across space and time to explore new characters and new possibilities. All fodder for building grand adventures.

Become a Writer for The Rifter®

We need new writers and artists to fill the next few decades of **The Rifter®**. You do not need to be a professional writer to contribute to **The Rifter®**. This publication is like a "fanzine," written by fans for fans. A forum in which gamers just like *you* can submit articles, G.M. advice, player tips, house rules, adventures, new magic, new psionics, new super abilities, monsters, villains, high-tech weapons, vehicles, power armor, short works of fiction and more. So think about writing up something short (even something as small as 4-6 pages). Newcomers and regular contributors are always welcome.

The Rifter® needs new material, especially when it comes to adventures and source material, for *all* of our game lines, particularly *Rifts®, Chaos Earth®, Palladium Fantasy RPG®, Heroes Unlimited™, Ninjas and Superspies™, Beyond the Supernatural™, Dead Reign®, Splicers®* and *Nightbane®*.

Pay is lousy, fame is dubious, but you see your work in print, get to share your ideas and adventures with fellow gamers, and get four free copies to show to your friends and family.

The Cover

The cover is by **Nick "The Brick" Bradshaw** and depicts a masked lunatic from the upcoming Dead Reign® sourcebook: In the Face of Death. Is he a hero or an oppressor? Or just plain crazy? You'll have to wait and see.

Optional and Unofficial Rules & Source Material

Most of the material for this issue is "official" source material. As for optional source material, settings and adventures, if they sound cool or fun, use them. If they sound funky, too high-powered or inappropriate for your game, modify them or ignore them completely. We hope all of it ignites your imagination and inspires you to create your own wonders.

www.palladiumbooks.com – Palladium Online

The Rifter® #80

One game system, infinite possibilities limited only by your imagination™

An unearthly tide washes over the planet.

A glimpse at what you can expect to see in Rifts® Sovietski. Art by Robert Atkins.

From the Desk of Kevin Siembieda

As I write this, mid-December, I'm also wrapping up work on **Rifts® Sovietski**. This is another fun, cool book with a lot of fun material on the Russia/Sovietski setting. It also includes some cool new D-Bees and O.C.C.s, a bunch of new combat vehicles, weapons and cyborgs, cool places to visit, and plenty of adventure hooks. You'll see a few familiar faces on artwork like *Charles Walton II* and *Ben Rodriguez*, both of whom just keep getting better and better, as well as *Mark Dudley,* who contributed in a bigger way than usual for this book. I'm hoping that's a trend he'll continue. You'll also see a couple of new names, both guys in the comic book business and who do spectacular artwork, *Robert Atkins* and *Steven Cummings.* You can expect to see more from these two artists in future books as well. Rifts Sovietski will be a fine addition to Rifts® that is sure to satisfy.

We are also in the middle of **Christmas Surprise Package** season. I have been loading them up and making them awesome. Probably a little too awesome, as most range from $96-$102 worth of goodies. But it's worth it every time we hear squeals of enjoyment and comments about how recipients have been blown away by the "awesome" Surprise Package. I started the Christmas Surprise Packages 19 years ago because I love Christmas and I wanted to do something to say thank you to our many wonderful fans around the world. It seemed like a great idea at the time and has since become a Christmas tradition. Our warehouse turns into Santa's workshop, filled with packages being shipped all over the world. It's pretty awesome and no small task. On a typical day, 3-4 of us will spend 4-5 hours working on picking, signing books, packing and shipping Surprise Packages. On a busy day, 4-5 of us will spend 7-9 hours processing orders. It's crazy but cool. Glad everyone is enjoying them so much.

By the way, there is still time to get a post-Christmas Surprise Package! As has become part of the Grab Bag tradition, we *extend* the Surprise package offer a few weeks *after* Christmas so people who didn't have the money then, or were too caught up in the holidays, can snag one afterward. You can order a Surprise Package up to *January 15, 2018,* and we will honor any mail order postmarked up to January 15, 2018. LAST CHANCE to get yours now!

Oh, my apologies about the occasional book in a Surprise Package that slips through without my signature. I know there have been at least three or four this season, not bad considering I typically sign around 8,000 books during the Surprise Package offer! This happens when I get called away or distracted in the middle of signing a stack of books and I lose my place and accidentally miss signing a book or two. I hope you're not too disappointed if that happens to you.

I am happy to sign it and any other books you may bring to any conventions that I attend, so don't hesitate to bring books for me and the guys to sign. In 2018 I'll be at **AdeptiCon** (March) in the Chicago area, then at the **Palladium Open House** (April 19-22) here in Westland at the Palladium warehouse, then at **Anime North** (May, Memorial Day weekend) in Toronto, and **Gen Con** (August) in Indianapolis. I'm considering a few other conventions, but if I hit too many we don't get enough books done.

Speaking of books, we expect the **Rifts® Bestiary™ Volume One** and **Rifts® Bestiary™ Volume Two** to quickly follow Sovietski, and then (in no exact order) **Dead Reign®: In the Face of Death™, CS Arsenal™** and **Disavowed**. The Bestiary books are being worked on right now. Gotta figure out what comes after that. We have a few **Splicers®, Palladium Fantasy RPG®, Rifts® Chaos Earth®** and **Rifts®** manuscripts waiting to see the light of day. Plus some big, special projects I want to surprise you with.

When we're not working on a book or Surprise Packages, there have been a wealth of projects we've been working on: the future of **Robotech® RPG Tactics**, and taking the game worlds you know and love into new mediums like film, television, video games and board games. Over the last couple of months there has been a lot of interest on the film and television front. With us fielding calls from 4 different producers or film companies regarding the availability of various Palladium I.P.s (intellectual properties), but nothing solid to report just yet. Fingers crossed. Everyone who has inquired are well known producers or companies, so it is exciting and humbling to be fielding inquiries and considering such possibilities. I just hope one or two of them actually come to something. I will keep you posted.

A plague has swept the office. I don't know if it is the flu, or a respiratory infection, or what, but some kind of bug has been running rampant through the office. First Julius, then Chuck, then Wayne, then Kathy, and those two were clobbered by it. I thought I had escaped, but it got me few days ago too. It is brutal, but it hasn't stopped me from putting in 10-12 hour days and working through the weekends to get books to the printer. What we are specifically working on at the moment, includes this issue of **The Rifter®** you hold in your hands, **Rifts® Sovietski** (an awesome new World Book), and the two **Rifts® Bestiary™** books, as well as planning and discussing a number of other books and projects.

Happy Holidays

As I write this, Hanukkah, Christmas, other holidays of similar tradition and the New Year are all coming up fast. It is a time of gift-giving, parties and joy. Drink in that joy. Cherish the good times and enjoy the people you love. I hope you all enjoyed the holiday season and a lot of good cheer. But remember, you don't need a holiday or special occasion to call your parents, brother, sister, and the people who matter most in your life to tell them know how much they mean to you. So do it. Remember to reach out and say hello and I love you. Your words will mean a great deal to them. Life is always bittersweet and much too short. With so many storms and disasters this year and now those terrible wildfires in California, count your blessings and be truly thankful for what you have and of the wonderful people in your lives who make life that much richer.

Know that our thoughts and warmest wishes are with all of you this and every holiday season, and all year long. You, our fans, mean the world to us. May your holidays have been truly magical, and the New Year full of good health, prosperity and joy.

– Kevin Siembieda, Publisher, Writer, and Surrogate Santa

Palladium News

By Kevin Siembieda, the guy who should know

Palladium Open House (POH)
Westland, Michigan – April 19-22, 2018

The Palladium Open House is only four months away! That means it will be here in no time at all. We already have a lot of people committed to attending, and we hope to get a lot more. Maybe our biggest POH attendance ever.

What we need is Game Masters and gaming events! Please do not wait to the last minute to send Palladium your game events and descriptions. If you are planning to run games at the 2018 POH, PLEASE let us know as soon as possible. This way we can put together a schedule a couple of months in advance of the actual event. Game Masters, contact us by email, phone or carrier pigeon but please get us your game info as soon as possible. Thank you. (By telephone (734-721-2903) or by email at **palladium-gm@palladiumbooks.com**.)

Game Masters who run *three or more games* **get a FREE special G.M. T-shirt** unveiled for the first time at the POH and a **30% Game Master Supreme Discount** on Palladium's RPG books, T-shirts and most other items. (Sorry, the discount does not apply to original art, limited editions, art prints, auction items and convention exclusive products.) We need plenty of games to satisfy 300 gamers, so your help is very appreciated and welcomed.

We expect to have more than 100 gaming events so we need experienced Game Masters to run Palladium events for all of our game lines – **Rifts®, Robotech®, Robotech® RPG Tactics™, Palladium Fantasy®, Heroes Unlimited™, Splicers®, Nightbane®, Dead Reign®, Beyond the Supernatural™**, and all the rest!

Contact us by telephone (734-721-2903) or by email at **palladium-gm@palladiumbooks.com** as SOON as possible. We want to post a schedule well in advance.

- **100+ Palladium gaming events.**
- **Price of admission pays for all events.**
- **Play in games run by Kevin Siembieda & other Palladium creators.**
- **Enjoy** *Robotech® RPG Tactics™* **tournaments, games, products and demos.**
- **Participate in** *panel talks* **and many question and answer chats.**
- **Bring your favorite game books to get signed.**
- **Meet** *Kevin Siembieda* **and the Palladium staff.**
- **Meet 30+ Palladium creators – the largest gathering of Palladium creators in the world! Most available every day, the entire day.**
- **Meet fellow gamers from around the world.**
- **Get new releases, back stock items and Palladium collectibles.**
- **Get original artwork, prints, T-shirts and specialty items.**
- **Intimate setting, unlike big conventions.**
- **Join the fun and make memories to last a lifetime.**

The POH (Palladium Open House) is four days (including VIP Thursday) of non-stop *Palladium gaming*. Thirty Palladium creators and personalities have confirmed they will attend, and we expect that number to grow! The Open House is always the largest gathering of Palladium creators and personalities anywhere in the world. The 2018 POH will include writers like *Carl Gleba, Carmen Bellaire, Brandon Aten, Greg Diaczyk*, artists like *John Zeleznik, Amy Ashbaugh, Chuck Walton, Mark Dudley* and me *(Kevin Siembieda)* and the entire *Palladium staff*. All of us will be available to hang out with you, chat, sign books, and many of us run game events. Yep, you get to game with the people who make the games at the place they are made.

The Palladium Open House is held only every 2-3 years, and we always strive to make it super-fun and memorable. Each has the feel of a family reunion and a weekend long party only with Palladium creators and gamers from around the world. I have to say, there is truly nothing quite like it. I think because we really are like a big family and because we really are happy to have you come and visit, and spend some time with us. Time doing some of our favorite things. See more details elsewhere in this book or at www.palladiumbooks.com

Our thanks to *Scott Gibbons* and *Kathy Simmons*, who are the two people most responsible for making this fan-favorite event a reality in 2018. We can't wait. It should be a blast.

X-Mas Surprise Package
extended to January 15, 2018

This is your last chance to snag a 2017 Surprise Package as a gift for a birthday, anniversary, Valentine's Day, graduation, or as a treat for yourself. A Surprise Package is an inexpensive way to try new games and new settings, fill holes in your collection, get caught up on The Rifter, or replace battered old books. Whatever the reason, order soon, because this offer is almost over.

What is a Palladium Christmas Surprise Package? It's a bargain and fun for you, and it's our way of saying thank you to our loyal fans by delivering a little Christmas cheer and putting smiles on the faces of some big kids around the world. We usually extend it an extra few weeks because we know that during the holiday season some of you are busy buying gifts for others and don't have money left to get anything for yourself. Others may have missed out because of all the demands of the holidays and some are just Johnny Come Latelies. Or maybe you just want to squeeze in one more. Well, this is your last chance.

$90-$95 (sometimes more) worth of Palladium Books products for only *$45 plus shipping and handling*. You are guaranteed to get an absolute minimum of *ninety dollars ($90) retail value* in your Surprise Package. Often you get $92-$95. Sometimes more! Santa Kevin likes to make gamers squeal with delight and often packs in $95-$100 worth of goodies into many Surprise Packages.

It's a surprise package because you never know *exactly* what you're going to get or who will sign your books. Sure the holidays have passed, but who doesn't like getting a nice surprise? We try to include many of the items on your "wish list," but we will surprise you with stuff you are not expecting. All items are "hand-picked" by *Kevin Siembieda* from your "wish lists." ALL with *autographs* if you request them. For many of you, this is the only way to get autographs from Kevin and available Palladium staff members, artists and writers! See more details elsewhere in this book or at www.palladiumbooks.com and you can order right now!

A bit of sad news

On November 26, 2017, Alex's mother, *Mary Marciniszyn*, passed away quietly into the night. She was 94 years old and had been frail and ailing for some time. She was comfortable and among loved ones in home hospice when she passed. Our love and heartfelt sympathy to *Alex, Diane, Vicky, Maryann, Nancy, Stephanie* and the rest of their family and friends. Take comfort in having had the rare privilege of a parent and grandparent in your life for such a very long time, and remember, she still lives inside each and every one of you.

A reminder why we need to hold and hug the people we love, and tell them how much they mean to us. Pick up your smart phone and don't just text, tweet or post on Facebook, but call your Mom, Dad, grandparents, siblings, and dear friends to tell them how much you care, and how important they are to you. Do it while you can. You never know what tomorrow may hold for you, or for them.

The Necronomnomnom

– Lovecraft-Inspired Cookbook

Our friend, *Thomas Roache* and his company, *Red Duke Games*, had a very successful Kickstarter for their **Necronomnomnom cookbook**. They needed something like $27,000 to make the product and raised $80,000! Congratulations, Tom! That's fantastic. I hope it continues to sell like crazy for you guys in bookstores after you fulfill your Kickstarter pledges next year. You deserve this.

Yes, AFTER they have fulfilled their Kickstarter obligations, Tom will be selling copies of the Necronomnomnon cookbook at conventions and online at Red Duke Games. And hopes to get it into bookstores in the future.

The Necronomnomnom, A Lovecraft-Inspired Cookbook is as cool as it sounds, and **Food & Wine Magazine** did an on-line article about it! The book's design is like that of an ancient tome with beautiful (and legible) script handwriting, dynamic artwork and diagrams, sepia pages, page after page of humor and spoof, and real, edible and delicious *food recipes*. This is a very cool coffee table book that gamers and fans of horror and fantasy should adore. Definitely a very cool item to own and a great gift for the wonderful home cooks (and horror/Cthulhu fans) you know.

The Kickstarter campaign is over, but you can still see what it looks like at: http://www.foodandwine.com/news/necronomnomnom-kickstarter

Rifts® Living Nowhere sourcebook

– postponed

Rifts® Living Nowhere has been postponed. The author is working on changes and it will probably be rescheduled as a summer or autumn 2018 release.

Coming Attractions

Palladium's 2017 Release Checklist

Available Now

- **New! The Rifter® #79 (new)** – 96 pages.
- **New! Nightbane® Dark Designs™ sourcebook** – 160 pages.
- **New! Rifts® Secrets of the Atlanteans™** – 224 pages, epic.
- **New! Rifts® Secrets of the Atlanteans™ Gold Hardcover** – 224 pages.
- **New! The Rifter® #78 (new)** – 96 pages.
- **The Rifter® #77** – 96 pages.
- **Rifts® Heroes of Humanity™** – 160 pages.

Coming Soon

- **Rifts® Sovietski™ World Book** – January, 2018, in production.
- **The Rifter® #80** – 96 pages – Winter/February, in production.
- **Rifts® Bestiary™ of North America, Volume One** – Winter (February).
- **Rifts® Bestiary™ of North America, Volume Two** – Winter (March).
- **Dead Reign® Sourcebook: In the Face of Death™** – December.
- **Rifts® The Disavowed™ Sourcebook by Kevin Siembieda and Matthew Clements**. Winter.
- **Rifts® Heroes of Humanity™ ARSENAL** – 96 or 128 pages – Spring.
- **Garden of the Gods™, a Palladium Fantasy RPG® Sourcebook by Kevin Siembieda** – Spring.

Also on the drawing board for 2018

- **Lopan™, a Palladium Fantasy RPG® Adventure Sourcebook**
- **Lopanic Games™, a Palladium Fantasy RPG® Sourcebook**
- **Robotech® RPG Ghost Fleet Saga Sourcebook**
- **Robotech® RPG Tactics™ Wave 2 expansion packs.**
- **Robotech® RPG Tactics™ Scenario Book One and adventures.**
- **Rifts® Haunted Tech™ sourcebook** – Rescheduled
- **Chaos Earth® First Responders**
- **Splicers® Sourcebooks**
- **Heroes Unlimited™ Sourcebooks**
- **Nightbane® Sourcebook**
- **Beyond the Supernatural™ Sourcebooks**
- **Rifts® World Books and Sourcebooks, including Rifts® New Navy, Rifts® Antarctica, and others.**

Palladium RPGs are available in many hobby and game stores around the world. We encourage people to support their local stores. Going to a store enables you to see the product before purchasing it, and many stores are happy to place special orders for you, provided you pay in advance, enabling you to avoid the cost of shipping and possible damage in the mail.

Ordering from Palladium Books: You can also order directly from Palladium Books, but you will pay extra for shipping. For customers with access to a computer, we highly recommend ordering online. This provides you with information about the most recent releases and Palladium's entire product catalog. It also provides you the most accurate shipping costs and more shipping options. You can also order by telephone; 734-721-2903 (order line only). For customers without such access, use the following "mail order" process.

1. Send the cost of the books or items being ordered.

2. In the USA: Add $6 for *orders* totaling $1-$50 to cover shipping and handling. Add $12 for *orders* totaling $51-$95. Add $18 for *orders* totaling $96-$200. **Note:** For *non-book products*, including the **Robotech® RPG Tactics™** box game and expansion packs, add an extra $6 per $50 worth of product, on top of the shipping amounts listed above. This is because *non-book products* cannot ship via Media Mail, and must use a more expensive method of shipping. **Outside the USA:** Double the shipping amount for orders going to Canada, and *quadruple* it for overseas orders. Any and all additional costs incurred as a result of customs fees and taxes are the responsibility of the foreign customer, NOT Palladium Books.

3. Make checks or money orders payable to *Palladium Books*.

4. Please make sure to send us your complete and correct address, *including* apartment number. **Note:** These costs are for the least expensive and slowest method of shipping only. Allow 2-4 weeks for delivery. Order online or call the office for a superior but more costly shipping method.

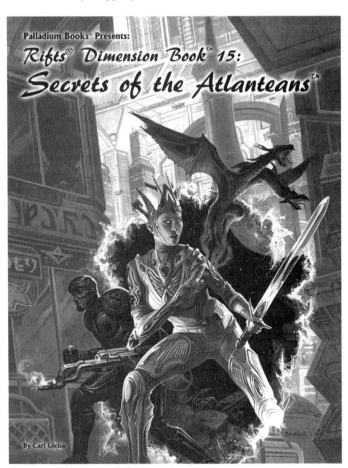

Rifts® Dimension Book™ 15:

Secrets of the Atlanteans™

People love this book. Available now. True Atlanteans are among the most mysterious and storied heroes across the Megaverse®. Learn about Atlantean civilization, the many clans,

where they are found across the Megaverse, why they hide, and why they hate the undead so much. Also discover the power of Shadow Magic, the treachery of the Sunaj Illuminati, and a darkness that could destroy them all.

- 60+ new Magic Tattoos.
- 60+ Shadow Magic spells.
- 30+ new Crystal Magic spells and the Crystal Mage O.C.C.
- Stone Pyramids described with floor plans.
- Stone Master and Undead Slayer, revisited.
- Sunaj Shadow Mage and Shadow Assassin O.C.C.s.
- The dark history, shame, and secrets of True Atlanteans.
- Learn more about the famous Atlantean Tattooed Warriors, Undead Slayers, Stone Masters and other Atlantean heroes.
- Tremble at the terrible secrets of the Aerihman and their plans for inter-dimensional domination.
- Dark secrets of the sinister Sunaj secret society.
- Who are the Sunaj and why do they hunt True Atlanteans?
- Valuable source material and adventure ideas galore.
- $24.95 retail for softcover edition – 224 pages – written by Carl Gleba – Cat. No. 890. Available now.

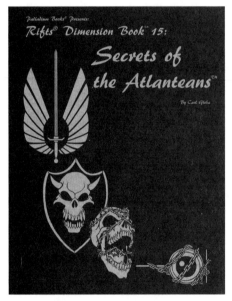

New! Secrets of the Atlanteans™ "Gold" Edition Hardcover

The deluxe hardcover "Gold" collector's edition, available now. The source material in **Rifts® Secrets of the Atlanteans™** is so awesome and the Atlanteans and Sunaj are so iconic, Palladium has made a limited edition, signed and numbered collector's hardcover. Contains the same source material as the softcover edition. Signed by the Palladium staff and limited to 300 copies.

- Black faux leather hardcover with metallic gold imprint.
- Signed by the Palladium staff.
- Numbered 1-300 and sold on a first come, first served basis. The number you receive is based on the order in which orders are received.
- 60+ new Magic Tattoos, 60+ Shadow Magic spells, 30+ new Crystal Magic spells, the Crystal Mage O.C.C., Stone Pyramids and everything in the softcover edition.
- $50.00 retail – 224 pages – written by Carl Gleba – Cat. No. 890HC – Available now.

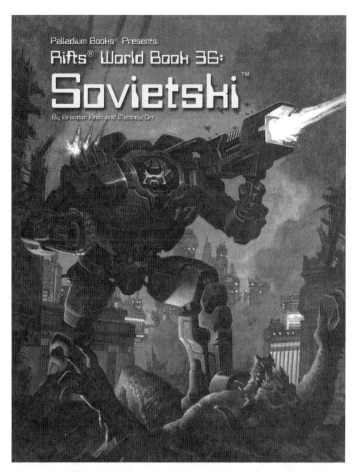

New! Nightbane® Dark Designs™

This is another title that people are enjoying and is available now. **Nightbane® Dark Designs™** is a guide to creating the Nightbane and a sourcebook for *players* and *Game Masters* alike. It presents all sorts of new Nightbane creation tables, new Morphus tables, new Talents, and new information. Info and powers that enable players to make memorable Nightbane characters and G.M.s to take their games up a notch.

- **18 new and comprehensive Morphus Tables.**
- **60 new Common Talents.**
- **38 new Elite Talents.**
- **Transformation Transition Table.**
- **Talent creation and conversion rules.**
- **Ancient Nightbane R.C.C. fully statted out and creation tables.**
- **Insight to the Becoming.**
- **Answers to some common questions & more.**
- **Appendix of 23 Morphus Tables gathered from the Nightbane® RPG and Sourcebooks.**
- **Appendix of 53 Talents gathered from the Nightbane® RPG and Sourcebooks.**
- **Written by Mark Oberle. Cover by Charles Walton II and Eduardo Dominguez.**
- **$20.95 – 160 pages – Cat. No. 736 – Available now.**

New! World Book 36: Rifts® Sovietski™

Nearly done and goes to the printer very soon.

Rifts® Sovietski™ delves into the new Soviet Nation, key places, people, O.C.C.s, combat vehicles, cyborgs, weapons and has everything you'd expect from a book like this. There is a wealth of information that will set your imagination on fire, new characters, new D-Bees, new weapons, vehicles and adventure hooks. There is the looming threat of General Goll's invasion of the Brodkil sent by Mindwerks' Angel of Death and Angel of Vengeance, treachery among the Warlords of Russia, and the coming of the Minion War. Learn about how the Sovietski came into being, its people's dreams, beliefs, politics, and its growing army, plus Deadzones, Spetsnaz Special Forces, new bionics, and more. And it all ties in nicely with the **Rifts® Mindwerks™ sourcebook, Warlords of Russia™** and **Mystic Russia™**.

- **New cyborgs and bionics.**
- **Sovietski war machine – tanks, aircraft, subs and more.**
- **Power armor, weapons, and gear.**
- **Spetsnaz Sovietski Special Forces and other O.C.C.s.**
- **Invasion by the *Brodkil Empire* and the Angel of Vengeance.**
- **Bunker creation tables and Deadzone tables.**
- **Russian D-Bees like Wolverine People and the elemental Yaga.**
- **Notable cities and other places of interest.**
- **Many adventure ideas and more.**
- **Written by Brandon Aten and Matthew Orr. Additional material by Kevin Siembieda.**
- **192 pages – $24.95 retail – Cat. No. 891. In final production. End of January or early February, 2018, release.**

New! Rifts® Bestiary™ of North America, Vol. One

You requested it, so we are doing it: collecting the hundreds of monsters and beasts of Rifts Earth into easy to use reference books, similar to what we did with *D-Bees of North America*. Only there are so many wondrous and fierce creatures we cannot squeeze them into one book. The first two **Rifts® Bestiary™ sourcebooks** are being created simultaneously, right now! Between them, these two volumes compile all the beasts of *Rifts North America* (unintelligent monsters, predators, notable animals and intelligent beings that are monstrous or animal-like in appearance or behavior) from all current World Books and Sourcebooks. In addition, Kevin Siembieda, Chuck Walton and Greg Diaczyk are adding some new monsters to make life in the wilderness interesting. Presented in alphabetical order, with maps showing their range and location, in two big books.

Note: If these two volumes do well, future volumes will include spirits, ghosts and entities, another on dragons, other volumes on creatures in other parts of Rifts Earth, and so on.

- Monsters and animals of Rifts North America organized in two big, easy to use sourcebooks. Predators, exotic riding animals, beasts of burden, alien horrors, giant insects and more.
- Some new creatures, but most are existing creatures.
- Updated information where applicable.
- Updated and uniform stat blocks.
- A map for every creature showing where it is found.
- Fully illustrated.
- Art by Chuck Walton, Siembieda and many others.
- 192-224 pages – $24.95 retail – Cat. No. 896. In production. Winter release. Anticipating Rifts® Bestiary™ Vol. One to be released in February, 2018.

New! Rifts® Bestiary™ of North America, Vol. Two

More monsters and exotic animals of Rifts® North America as part of an ongoing series of **Rifts® Bestiary sourcebooks**. The first two **Rifts® Bestiaries, Volume One** and **Volume Two**, are being created simultaneously. Between them, these two volumes compile all the beasts of *Rifts North America* (unintelligent monsters, predators, notable animals and intelligent beings that are monstrous or animal-like in appearance or behavior) from all current World Books and Sourcebooks, plus some new monsters by Siembieda and Walton. Presented in alphabetical order, with maps showing their range and location, in two big books. **Note:** If these two volumes do well, more will follow.

- Monsters and animals of Rifts North America organized in two big, easy to use sourcebooks. Predators, exotic riding animals, beasts of burden, alien horrors, giant insects and more.
- Some new creatures, but most are existing creatures.
- Updated information where applicable.
- Updated and uniform stat blocks.
- A map for every creature showing where it is found.
- Fully illustrated.
- Art by Chuck Walton, Siembieda and many others.
- 192-224 pages – $24.95 retail – Cat. No. 897. In production. Winter release. Anticipating Rifts® Bestiary™ Vol. Two to be out by the end of March, 2018.

COMING!

In the Face of Death™

– A Dead Reign® Sourcebook

This sourcebook is all about inner city survival. Survivor colonies finding a way to live and prosper in the big city. Conventional wisdom is living in the big population centers is impossible. These survivors prove otherwise.

- Inner city survival. Old and new O.C.C.s.
- Skyscraper communities and life on the rooftops.
- Cults – the new power in the city.
- Gangs, street runners, the new underground, and more.
- Take your zombie campaign to new heights!
- Cover by E.M. Gist. Interior art by Nick Bradshaw.
- Written by Kevin Siembieda. Adaptable to other Palladium settings.
- Size and price not yet determined – Cat. No. 237. Winter, 2018.

And Don't Forget . . .

Dead Reign® RPG. It is the aftermath of the *zombie apocalypse*. Civilization is gone, the dead reign, and the living fight to survive against impossible odds. Tales of zombies, human survival and horror as a fast-paced, easy to learn game and sourcebooks.

- Zombie combat rules, vehicles and equipment.
- Six iconic Apocalyptic Character Classes and Ordinary People with 40+ occupations to choose from.
- Seven types of zombies plus the Half-Living.
- Secrets of the Dead and tips on fighting zombies.

- Death Cults, their Priests, power over zombies and goals.
- 101 Random Scenarios, Encounters and Settings.
- 100 Random Corpse Searches and other tables.
- Quick Roll Character Creation tables (10 minutes).
- A complete role-playing game by Siembieda and others.
- $24.95 retail – 224 pages – Cat. No. 230. Available now.

Dead Reign® Sourcebook Two: Dark Places™. Secrets of survival, including using railroad tracks and the urban underground to travel unseen and undetected by zombies.
- Worm Meat, Bug Boy, Sewer Crawler and Impersonator Zombies.
- "Live Bait" zombie lures with human beings as bait.
- Traveling the rails and boxcar encounter tables.
- Traveling sewer tunnels, steam tunnels & other dark places.
- The pitfalls and dangers of the urban underground.
- Diseases, infection and additional world information.
- Random encounter tables, boxcar content tables, and more.
- $12.95 retail – 64 pages – Cat. No. 232. Available now.

Dead Reign® Sourcebook One: Civilization Gone™. It has been months since the dead rose to attack the living. Civilization has crumbled. There is no army, no government, no help coming. You are on your own and things are only getting worse.
- Madmen and Psychopaths including the *Zombie Master, Ghost Walker, Backstabber, Messianic Leader, Zombie Lover, Deathbringer* and others.
- *Bandits* and *Raiders* who prey upon other survivors.
- *Street Gang Protectors* and their mission to save lives.
- Phobia and Obsession tables. Many adventure ideas.
- House and home resource and encounter tables.
- Random encounter and survivor camp creation tables.
- Additional world information and survival advice.
- $12.95 retail – 64 pages – Cat. No. 231. Available now.

Dead Reign® Sourcebook 3: Endless Dead™. The zombie hordes grow in number and strangeness. Can humankind survive? Where is the military?
- New types of zombies like Fused Zombies and the Walking Mass Grave.
- New O.C.C.s including Wheelman, Zombie Hunter & Zombie Researcher.
- Info & tables for weaponizing vehicles and vehicle combat rules.

- **Random encounter tables for military bases, police stations, gun stores, buildings, suburbs, industrial parks, small towns, farmland and wilderness.**
- **Tables for creating Survivor caravans, hideouts, Safe Havens & more.**
- **Timetable for setting zombie campaigns and many adventure ideas.**
- **$16.95 retail – 96 pages – Cat. No. 233. Available now.**

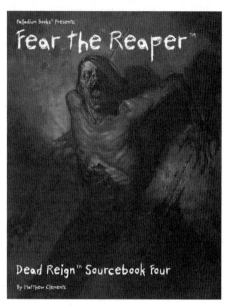

Dead Reign® Sourcebook 4: Fear The Reaper™. Everything you could want to know about the heroic Road Reapers. Heroes who, like knights of old, travel the highways and byways to fight zombies and help survivors.
- **Comprehensive background on the legendary Road Reapers.**
- **Their code, missions, strategies and tactics.**
- **Areas of specializations, notable weapons and gear.**
- **The Terror Zombie and more.**
- **$12.95 retail – 48 pages – Cat. No. 234. Available now.**

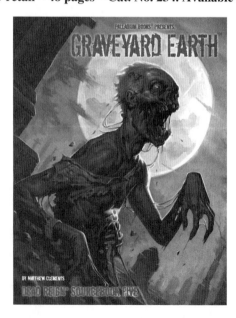

Dead Reign® Sourcebook 5: Graveyard Earth™. This expansive world book takes a look at the Zombie Apocalypse and how survivors are faring around the globe. Every country in the world has been changed by the rise of the dead. This sourcebook gives you that overview of the world.
- **Many random tables, encounters and adventure ideas set around the world.**
- **Random Safe Havens by region.**
- **How to get home from abroad, zombie threat levels and more.**
- **Timetable for setting zombie campaigns and many adventure ideas.**
- **$12.95 retail – 64 pages – Cat. No. 235. Available now.**

A Dead Reign® Sourcebook: Hell Followed™. This book begins to redefine the zombie genre. It broadens the field of possibilities and expands upon the modern zombie mythos. It is full of twists and surprises you will not see coming. Be more than a survivor. Do something about it.
- **11 new types of zombies.**
- **7 new Apocalyptic Character Classes.**
- **Masked Lunatics – heroes or madmen?**
- **Cults, good and bad, plus other weirdness and dangers.**
- **21 disasters to complicate survival.** Each described with damage stats, penalties and consequences. The most comprehensive information of this type ever presented! Suitable for any game world.
- **Government enclaves and conspiracy theories, and creation rules.**
- **Abandoned Emergency Relief Centers** and the resources they offer.
- **$20.95 retail – 160 pages – Cat. No. 236. Available now.**

COMING! The Rifter® #80
– Ships February, 2018

The Rifter® #80 is already in development. Articles are being selected and artwork is being assigned.

Every issue of The Rifter® is an *idea factory* for players and Game Masters to generate new ideas and find new avenues of adventure. It provides useful, ready to go source material you can just drop into your ongoing games. A doorway to new possibilities and numerous Palladium role-playing worlds. And the many new characters, O.C.C.s, powers, magic, weapons, villains, monsters, adventures and ideas for one setting can be easily adapted to *any* Palladium setting. Every issue has material for **Rifts®** and usually 2-3 other Palladium game lines. The focus of this issue is **Rifts®**, **Splicers®** and RPG advice. Don't forget, unofficial material can be easily adapted for use in ANY Palladium game setting.

Rifter® #80 Highlights:

- **Rifts®** – source material.
- **Splicers®** source material.
- **Palladium Fantasy RPG®** source material.
- **Heroes Unlimited™** source material.
- News, coming attractions, product descriptions and more.
- 96 pages – $13.95 retail – Cat. No. 180. Winter, 2018. Anticipating a February release.

COMING! Rifts® The Disavowed™

Secrets of the Coalition States™

"Desperate times require desperate measures. War has nothing to do with morality or justice. It's all about winning or dying. We cannot bind our hands with high ideals, even our own, or worry about the laws of renegade nations or the rights of alien people. We must fight fire with fire. And you are the match." – *Colonel Lyboc addressing a Disavowed team*

The Disavowed are so Top Secret that their existence is known only to a handful of the Coalition States' most elite, top echelon, with *Joseph Prosek II* the mastermind behind the Disavowed operation, and Colonel Lyboc its shadowy face. Find out who these men and women are. How the Disavowed get away with using magic, traveling to other parts of Rifts Earth and even to other dimensions in pursuit of enemies and strategic information that cannot be had through conventional means. Learn about the secret parameters in which these hard-boiled warriors, secretly hand-picked by Joseph Prosek II, operate, why almost every mission is considered a suicide mission, and why they must forever be the Disavowed.

- CS operatives so secret that even the top military and political leaders right up to Emperor Prosek *know nothing about them*. And if they did know, would they condone their activity or condemn it?
- Are the Disavowed heroes or renegades? Assassins or soldiers? Madmen or super-patriots? Or a little of them all?
- Unsung heroes who keep the CS safe, or thugs and pawns of a shadow agency within the Coalition government?
- What role does the Vanguard play in this group?
- How do they reward their D-Bee "teammates" when the mission is over?
- What happens to the Disavowed when they have seen or learned too much? Adventure ideas galore and so much more.
- Written by Kevin Siembieda and Matthew Clements.
- 96 pages – $16.95 retail – Cat. No. 892. Winter.

COMING!

Heroes of Humanity™ *CS Arsenal*

Rifts® Secrets of the Coalition States™ Sourcebook

Rifts® Heroes of Humanity gave you updated Coalition Army O.C.C.s, ways to upgrade men-at-arms, new O.C.C.s, battle plans and strategies and tactics. **CS Arsenal** provides an array of new Coalition hardware: weapons, armor, additional SAMAS, other power armor, robots, combat vehicles, gear and info.

- New CS weapons and gear, like the Glitter Boy Boom Tank.
- New CS SAMAS and power armor.
- New CS robots and combat vehicles.
- More secrets and information about the Coalition States.
- Wild adventure opportunities, fun and more.
- Part of the *Minion War™ "Crossover" series*.
- Written by Kevin Siembieda, Clements, Gleba and others.
- 96 pages – $16.95 retail – Cat. No. 893. Winter.

COMING! Rifts® Living Nowhere™

– A Rifts® Sourcebook set in the Pecos Empire

This title presents three interrelated towns off the beaten path in the Pecos Empire. Each with its own unique character and problems. All fun locations to visit and find adventure and trouble. Something dark and deadly is brewing in the middle of Nowhere, where experimental Techno-Wizard devices and weapons offer prosperity, but could be the doom of everyone living there. Big ideas. Building upon material that appeared in The Rifter®, expanded.

- Three towns described.
- New Techno-Wizard weapons and devices.
- Experimental Techno-Wizard items that call upon entropy and death.
- Dark magic, madness and deadly secrets spawn dangerous adventures.
- Many adventure ideas, Non-Player Characters, and fun.
- Written by Brett Caron. Additional text and ideas by Kevin Siembieda.
- 96 pages – $16.95 retail – Cat. No. 895. Summer or fall, 2018.

COMING! Garden of the Gods™

A Palladium Fantasy RPG® Sourcebook

This has been a secret project of Kevin Siembieda's that he has been plotting and writing in what little spare time he has. *The Garden of the Gods* is said to be a holy place watched over and even frequented by the avatars of the gods. According to legend, the god may visit heroes and followers in dreams or in person by an avatar of the god, to be given guidance, inspiration, heroic quests, and gifts of knowledge and magic. More details about this title will follow, but he is actively writing this title, splitting his time between it and the Rifts® titles above.

- The Garden of the Gods described in detail.
- Godly insight and visitations.
- Gifts of magic and knowledge.
- Sanctuary and more.
- The Black Pit, a place of evil and dark secrets. Is it a counterbalance to the good of the Garden or a trick of the Old Ones?
- Written by Kevin Siembieda.
- Final page count, price and catalog number yet to be determined, but probably 96 or 128 pages – $16.95 retail. Spring, 2018.

2017 Christmas Surprise Package

Extended till January 15, 2018

Accepting **Surprise Package** orders now through **January 15, 2018.** We extend it for a short time *after* Christmas for those of you who missed it or would like to get one last Surprise.

What is a Palladium Christmas Surprise Package?

● **$90-$100 worth of Palladium products for only $45 (plus shipping and handling)!** That can nab you four or more items when one core rule book can cost you more that. What a deal!

● **Autographs** from Kevin Siembieda, available staff and freelance artists and writers. If you "request" autographs we'll sign *every* book in your box! For many, especially those across the country and overseas, this is the *only* way to get autographs from Kevin Siembieda and crew. *Take advantage of it.*

If you do NOT want autographs, please state – "No autographs."

If you do NOT want T-shirts, please write – "No T-shirts."

● **Each order is hand-picked by** *Kevin Siembieda* from a "wish list" *you* provide! Please list at least **10-15 items** that you know are in stock. PLEASE do not list books you know are *out of print*; you will not get them. **Note:** List 8 or fewer titles and your order may be rejected or you will get items not on your list.

● **The Grab Bag makes a wonderful gift for** Christmas, Hanukkah, birthdays, anniversaries, etc., for the gamers in your life. Since there will be so much in every Surprise Package, ordering just one might provide gifts for two or more pals.

● **Impress your friends with a gift worth $90** *or more* for a cost of only $45 (plus shipping and handling).

● **Fill holes in your own collection** or get books and product you've been meaning to try or have been eyeballing.

It's a surprise package because you never know exactly what you're going to get or who will sign your books. We try to include *many* of the items on your "wish list," but we may surprise you with stuff you are not expecting. Extra items may include other *RPG books, The Rifter®, posters, prints, art books, greeting cards, T-shirts,* and other items. Some may be slightly damaged so we can send you more.

Spread the word. The Christmas Surprise Package is only publicized by word of mouth, to readers of **The Rifter®** and on **Palladium's website – www.palladiumbooks.com –** so *tell everyone you know.* Buy one for *every gamer you know* and *have a very Merry Christmas.*

Multiple orders WILL result in some duplication.

The Cost

$45.00 plus $10.00 for shipping and handling in the USA; $55 total.

$45.00 plus $30.00 estimated for shipping and handling to CANADA; $75 total.

$45.00 plus $52.00 estimated for shipping and handling OVERSEAS; $97 total. **Note:** Sorry, we are only passing along the postal rates of Priority Mail International (typically 4-10 days delivery). We always try to load up on orders going overseas, so you can expect at least $100 worth of product with *autographs* and items you might not normally be able to get.

All domestic orders are shipped U.S.P.S., Media Mail (the "slow" Book Rate), or UPS, <u>or</u> the way *Palladium* chooses. Ordering online, you select the desired method of shipping and pay accordingly. We strongly suggest **UPS** because it is fast, reliable and trackable. *Media Mail* takes 7-21 days to arrive, and one-of-a-kind items like gold editions can <u>NOT</u> be replaced if lost.

Credit card orders welcomed. ALL major credit cards accepted. Order by mail, telephone or online.

No C.O.D. orders.

We must have YOUR *street address* (no P.O. Box) for *UPS.*

We need your entire, correct street address and APARTMENT NUMBER! Palladium is NOT responsible for loss if you give us an *incorrect* or *incomplete address*, or if you *move* <u>after</u> you place the order.

Note: Orders received by Palladium after *December 14th CANNOT* be *guaranteed* to arrive *before Christmas.* Palladium makes no promise that foreign or military base orders will be received before December 25th regardless of when they are placed. Rare books and one-of-a-kind items, like art prints or gold editions, CANNOT be replaced if lost in the mail.

Send Mail Orders to: *Palladium Books – Dept. X – 39074 Webb Court – Westland, MI 48185-7606.* **Or order online** in our online store at *www.palladiumbooks.com* – or call **(734) 721-2903 to place orders by telephone** using a credit card.

Ideas for "Special Wants"

To insure your X-Mas Surprise Package is everything you want it to be, send us a *wish list* of your "wants." **The more items listed**, the more likely you are to get items *you want.* List them in order of preference (10-15 items you know are in stock). That way, you don't know what you're getting and we have a large selection to choose from, making it fun for you and easier on us. Thanks.

PLEASE do *not* ask for books you *know* are not yet available or are out of print like *Tome Grotesque* or *Mechanoid Space®.*

Note: Santa Kev and his elves are NOT mind readers. If you do not give us a clear idea of your wants, you *may* be disappointed by what comes in your Surprise Package. You do NOT make our job easier when you say something like "I own everything, surprise me." Please provide 10-15 items! And you may still get items not on your list.

● **Rifts® Ultimate Edition** and core books like **Rifts® Book of Magic, Rifts® G.M. Guide,** and **Rifts® Adventure Guide.**

● For Chaos Earth®: **Chaos Earth® RPG, Rise of Magic, Creatures of Chaos,** and **Chaos Earth® Resurrection.**

● For Rifts®: **Rifts® Secrets of the Atlanteans, Coalition States: Heroes of Humanity, Megaverse® in Flames, Rifts® Vampires Sourcebook, Rifts® Lemuria, Triax™ 1 & 2, D-Bees of North America, Adventures in Dinosaur Swamp, The Vanguard™, Heroes of the Megaverse®, Rifts® Machinations of Doom™** (graphic novel & sourcebook), **Tales of the Chi-Town 'Burbs™** (short stories), **Rifts® & the Megaverse®** (softcover art book), **Rifts® Coloring Book, World Book 2: Atlantis, Africa, Triax & the NGR, Rifts® South America, Juicer Uprising™, Coalition War Campaign, Federation of Magic™, Psyscape™, Rifts® Australia, Rifts® Mercenaries,**

Rifts® MercTown™, Rifts® Merc Adventures, the Siege on Tolkeen/Coalition Wars® series & more!

Looking for *high-tech?* Consider Rifts® Game Master Guide, Naruni™ Wave 2, Coalition War Campaign™, Coalition Navy™, Heroes of Humanity, Northern Gun™ Two, Black Market, Triax & the NGR™, Triax™ 2, Rifts® Merc-Town, New West™, Atlantis, and others.

Want Rifts® NPCs? Then Rifts® Siege on Tolkeen Six: Final Siege is a must: 31 NPCs and 11 dragons fully statted out, plus monsters, TW, maps and city of Tolkeen, and more. SoT5: Shadows of Evil has 16 more NPCs.

Looking for magic and monsters? Consider Rifts® Federation of Magic™, Machinations of Doom™, Atlantis, Secrets of the Atlanteans, South America Two, Rifts® Spirit West™, Lemuria, Mystic Russia.

Emphasis on monsters and D-Bees: Rifts® Conversion Books 1, 2 & 3, D-Bees of North America™, Psyscape™, New West™, Rifts® Dinosaur Swamp™, *Adventures* in Dinosaur Swamp™, Splynn Dimensional Market™, Phase World®, Hades, Dyval™ & others.

For space adventure, see Phase World®, Phase World® Sourcebook and Dimension Books™ like Thundercloud Galaxy™, Skraypers™, Heroes of the Megaverse®, Megaverse® Builder™, Anvil Galaxy, Three Galaxies™.

● For the Minion War™, see Megaverse® in Flames, CS Heroes of Humanity, Hades, Dyval™, Dimensional Outbreak™, Heroes of the Megaverse®, Armageddon Unlimited™.

● Rifts® Dimension Books™ are always fun: Megaverse® Builder™, Heroes of the Megaverse®, Thundercloud Galaxy™, Naruni™ Wave 2, Wormwood™, Skraypers™, Phase World® Sourcebook, Three Galaxies™, and others.

● Rifts® Conversion Books include Rifts® Conversion Book One, Book 2: Pantheons of the Megaverse® & Dark Conversions™.

● Robotech®. Get the Robotech® Expeditionary Force Marines Sourcebook, the Robotech® RPG Hardcover (or pocket-sized RPG), and these Robotech® Sourcebooks: Macross® Saga, The Masters Saga™, New Generation™, and Genesis Pits™.

● Robotech® RPG Tactics™ Main Box Set – The core box game with 30+ game pieces, rule book, 50+ cards, 24 dice and more. $99.95 value, so *if* you get one, it *is the ONLY item* you will receive!

● Robotech® RPG Tactics™ Expansion Packs – For the Grab Bag, these items all have a value of $40 each. Macross mecha.

● Heroes Unlimited™ superhero gaming! Powers Unlimited™ 1, 2 & 3, HU2™ G.M.'s Guide, Gramercy Island™, Villains Unlimited™ Revised, Aliens Unlimited™, Aliens Unlimited™ Galaxy Guide™, Armageddon Unlimited™, Mystic China™, After the Bomb® sourcebooks. Heroes of the Megaverse® and Skraypers™ are HU2 adaptable.

● Palladium Fantasy RPG® and sourcebooks. A unique fantasy world with human and non-human races like the Wolfen. Palladium Fantasy RPG®, and sourcebooks like Bizantium™, Western Empire™, Northern Hinterlands™, Land of the Damned™ One and Two, Mysteries of Magic™ One, Eastern Territory™, and others.

● Dead Reign® RPG, the zombie apocalypse – Endless Dead™, Graveyard Earth™, Civilization Gone™, Dark Places™, Fear the Reaper™, Hell Followed™. *Zombies can be used in any setting.*

● Beyond the Supernatural™ RPG: Modern day horror & monsters.

● Nightbane® RPG and Dark Designs™ (new!), Nightbane® Survival Guide, Through the Glass Darkly and others. Can be used with *Heroes Unlimited™, Ninjas & Superspies™,* and *Beyond the Supernatural™.*

● Back Stock: Get RPGs, sourcebooks, and world books you've been wanting or fill holes in your collection.

● Try new game settings like Robotech®, Splicers®, Dead Reign®, Rifts®, Palladium Fantasy®, Nightbane®, Heroes Unlimited™, Ninjas & Superspies™, Beyond the Supernatural™, Chaos Earth®, After the Bomb®, The Mechanoid® Trilogy, or RECON®.

● *Rifter®* back issues are available (issues 1-13 only in the X-Mas Surprise Package). Many issues are sold out, including issues #4, #8, #18-26, #28-35, #40, #46-48, and others.

● Art Books include Future Visions™ (Charles Walton art, b/w), Rifts® & the Megaverse® (Zeleznik art, color), Zeleznik Coloring Book, and Rifts® Machinations of Doom™ (Perez; graphic novel & sourcebook).

● Art Prints – black & white and color prints, Rifts® and fantasy maps (various, color), Dog Boys Playing Poker, Rifts® (various) and others; average value of $5-$10 each.

● Novelty Items. Bookmarks Set #1 & #2, greeting cards, mouse pads (for Rifts®, Dead Reign®, Fantasy), Rifts® Chi-Town 'Burbs Anthology, T-shirts, A+Plus comic books, etc.

Ordering the 2017 Surprise Package

Include *ALL* of the following information . . .

● *Special Wants* – list 10-15 specific items/books, new and old, or items like prints or T-shirts, etc.
● Indicate "No T-shirt" if you don't want to be considered for one. If you *DO WANT* a T-shirt, include *your size.*
● Your favorite Palladium games.
● Palladium games you have *not* played but want to try.
● Indicate whether you want autographs.
● Comments and suggestions.
● Accurate & complete mailing address! UPS cannot ship to a P.O. Box; provide a *street* address. Include your APARTMENT number! Palladium is NOT responsible for *loss* if you give us an *incorrect* or *incomplete address*, or if you *move.*

Total Cost: $55 USA ($45.00 + $10 estimated for shipping & handling), $75 to Canada, $97 overseas. Multiple orders *will* result in duplication. This is a "Grab Bag" so you may get items not on your Wish List.

Credit cards are welcomed: Visa and MasterCard preferred, but most major credit cards are accepted. Go to the Palladium website (www.palladiumbooks.com) and fill out the 2017 Christmas Surprise Package Order Form and pay with a credit card. Or order by telephone (734-721-2903); this is an *order line* only.

Place orders by mail by enclosing a check or money order along with your wish list, the info above *and address*, and send to:

Palladium Books® – Dept. X – 39074 Webb Court – Westland, MI 48185, USA

K. SIEMBIEDA 2015

Palladium Books® Check List

The Rifter® Series
___ 176 The Rifter® #76 – $13.95
___ 177 The Rifter® #77 – $13.95
___ 178 The Rifter® #78 – $13.95
___ 179 The Rifter® #79 – $13.95
___ 180 The Rifter® #80 – $13.95 (coming)

Splicers®   Note: Sourcebooks coming soon.
___ 200 Splicers® RPG – $23.95

Dead Reign®
___ 230 Dead Reign® RPG – $24.95
___ 231 SB 1: Civilization Gone™ – $12.95
___ 232 SB 2: Dark Places™ – $12.95
___ 233 SB 3: Endless Dead™ – $16.95
___ 234 SB 4: Fear the Reaper™ – $12.95
___ 235 SB 5: Graveyard Earth™ – $12.95
___ 236 SB 6: Hell Followed™ – $20.95
___ 237 SB 7: In the Face of Death™ – $16.95

Rifts® Novels
___ 301 Sonic Boom™ – $9.95
___ 302 Deception's Web™ – $9.95
___ 303 Treacherous Awakenings™ – $9.95
___ 304 Tales of the Chi-Town 'Burbs™ – $12.95
___ 305 Rifts® Path of the Storm™ – $12.95

Weapons Books
___ 401 Weapons and Armor™ – $8.95
___ 402 Weapons and Castles™ – $8.95
___ 403 Weapons and Assassins™ – $9.95
___ 404 Weapons & Castles of the Orient™ – $9.95
___ 409 Exotic Weapons™ – $9.95
___ 410 European Castles™ – $9.95

Palladium Fantasy RPG®
___ 450 The Palladium Fantasy RPG® – $26.95
___ 4500HC Palladium Fantasy RPG® 30th Anniversary Hardcover – $50.00
___ 451 Dragons & Gods™ – $24.95
___ 453 Old Ones™ 2nd Ed. – $24.95
___ 454 Monsters & Animals™ 2nd Ed. – $24.95
___ 455 Adventures on the High Seas™ – $24.95
___ 458 Island at the Edge of the World™ – $20.95
___ 459 Yin-Sloth Jungles™ – $20.95
___ 462 Western Empire™ – $24.95
___ 463 Baalgor Wastelands™ – $24.95
___ 464 Mount Nimro™ – $20.95
___ 465 Eastern Territory™ – $24.95
___ 466 Library of Bletherad™ – $20.95
___ 467 Northern Hinterlands™ – $24.95
___ 468 Land/Damned 1: Chaos Lands™ – $24.95
___ 469 LoD 2: Eternal Torment™ – $24.95
___ 470 LoD 3: The Citadel – $24.95 (coming)
___ 471 Wolfen Empire™ – $20.95
___ 472 Mysteries of Magic™ One: Heart of Magic – $16.95
___ 474 Bizantium/Northern Islands™ – $20.95
___ 475 Garden of the Gods™ – $16.95 (coming)

Heroes Unlimited™ / After the Bomb®
___ 500-2 Heroes Unlimited™, 2nd Ed. – $26.95
___ 5000HC Heroes Unlimited™ 30th Anniversary Hardcover – $50.00
___ 501 Villains Unlimited™ Revised – $24.95
___ 503 After the Bomb® RPG – $24.95
___ 505 Road Hogs™ (After the Bomb® II) – $9.95
___ 507 Mutants Down Under™ (AB III) – $9.95
___ 511 Mutants of the Yucatan™ (AB IV) – $9.95
___ 513 Mutants in Avalon™ (AB V) – $16.95
___ 514 Mutants in Orbit™ (AB VI) – $16.95
___ 515 Aliens Unlimited™ – $24.95
___ 516 Heroes Unlimited™ G.M.'s Guide – $24.95
___ 517 Century Station™ – $24.95
___ 518 Gramercy Island™ – $24.95
___ 519 Aliens Unlimited Galaxy Guide™ – $24.95
___ 520 Mutant Underground™ – $16.95
___ 521 Powers Unlimited® One – $16.95
___ 522 Powers Unlimited® Two – $16.95
___ 523 Powers Unlimited® Three – $16.95
___ 525 Revised Ninjas & Superspies™ – $20.95
___ 526 Mystic China™ – $24.95
___ 527 Armageddon Unlimited™ – $20.95

Robotech® RPG
___ 550 Robotech® The Shadow Chronicles® RPG (manga size) – $16.95
___ 550HC Robotech® The Shadow Chronicles® Deluxe Hardcover RPG – $30.95
___ 5500HC Robotech® The Shadow Chronicles® Gold Ed. Hardcover RPG – $70.00
___ 551 Robotech® Macross® Saga Sourcebook – $16.95
___ 552 Robotech® The Masters Saga™ Sourcebook (NEW in 8½ x 11) – $20.95
___ 553 Robotech®: Expeditionary Force Marines Sourcebook – $20.95
___ 554 Robotech® The New Generation™ Sourcebook – $16.95
___ 555 Robotech® Genesis Pits Sourcebook – $16.95

Robotech® RPG Tactics™ (New!)
___ 55100 Robotech® RPG Tactics™ – $99.95
___ 55105 Robotech® RPG Tactics™ Rulebook – $20.00
___ 55101 UEDF Dice Pack – $12.00
___ 55102 Zentraedi Dice Pack – $12.00
___ 55201 UEDF Valkyrie Wing – $36.95
___ 55202 UEDF Destroid Pack – $32.95
___ 55203 UEDF Spartan Pack – $32.95
___ 55401 Zentraedi Regult Battlepods – $36.95
___ 55402 Zentraedi Artillery Battlepods – $36.95
___ 55403 Zentraedi Glaug Command – $36.95

Rifts® Chaos Earth®
___ 660 Rifts® Chaos Earth® RPG – $20.95
___ 661 Rifts® CE Creatures of Chaos™ – $12.95
___ 662 Rifts® CE The Rise of Magic™ – $12.95
___ 665 Rifts® Chaos Earth® First Responders™ – $16.95 (coming)
___ 666 Rifts® Chaos Earth® Resurrection™ – $20.95

Beyond the Supernatural™
___ 700 Beyond the Supernatural™, 2nd Ed. – $24.95
___ 702 Tome Grotesque™ – $20.95 (coming)
___ 703 Beyond Arcanum™ – $24.95 (coming)

Nightbane®
___ 730 Nightbane® RPG – $24.95
___ 731 Nightbane®: Between the Shadows™ – $20.95
___ 732 Nightbane®: Nightlands™ – $20.95
___ 733 Nightbane®: Through the Glass Darkly™ – $20.95
___ 735 Nightbane® Survival Guide™ – $20.95
___ 736 Nightbane® Dark Designs™ – $20.95

Rifts®
___ 800HC Rifts® RPG Ultimate Edition – $39.95
___ 801 Rifts® Sourcebook One Revised – $20.95
___ 802-E Rifts® World Book 1: Vampire Kingdoms™, Revised – $24.95
___ 803 Rifts® Conversion Book One™ – $24.95
___ 804 Rifts® WB 2: Atlantis™ – $20.95
___ 805 Rifts® Sourcebook 2: Mechanoids™ – $16.95
___ 807 Rifts® WB 3: England™ – $20.95
___ 808 Rifts® WB 4: Africa™ – $20.95
___ 809 Rifts® Dimension Book 1: Wormwood™ – $20.95
___ 810 Rifts® WB 5: Triax™ – $24.95
___ 811 Rifts® Pantheons of the Megaverse® – $24.95
___ 812 Rifts® Sourcebook 3: Mindwerks™ – $16.95
___ 813 Rifts® Mercenaries™ – $20.95
___ 814 Rifts® WB 6: South America – $20.95
___ 815 Rifts® WB 7: Underseas™ – $24.95
___ 816 Rifts® DB 2: Phase World® – $24.95
___ 817 Rifts® DB 3: Phase World® Sourcebook – $16.95
___ 818 Rifts® WB 8: Rifts® Japan™ – $24.95
___ 819 Rifts® WB 9: South America Two™ – $24.95
___ 820 Rifts® WB 10: Juicer Uprising™ – $20.95
___ 821 Rifts® WB 11: Coalition War Campaign™ – $24.95
___ 822 Rifts® WB 12: Psyscape™ – $20.95
___ 825 Rifts® WB 13: Lone Star™ – $20.95

___ 826 Rifts® WB 14: New West™ – $24.95
___ 827 Rifts® WB 15: Spirit West™ – $24.95
___ 828 Rifts® Sourcebook 4: Coalition Navy™ – $16.95
___ 829 Rifts® WB 16: Federation of Magic™ – $20.95
___ 830 Rifts® DB 4: Skraypers™ – $20.95
___ 831 Rifts® Index Volume Two™ – $16.95
___ 832 Rifts® WB 17: Warlords of Russia™ – $24.95
___ 833 Rifts® WB 18: Mystic Russia™ – $20.95
___ 834 Rifts® WB 19: Australia 1 – $24.95
___ 835 Rifts® WB 20: Canada™ – $24.95
___ 836 Rifts® WB 21: Splynn Dimensional Market™ – $24.95
___ 837 Rifts® WB 22: Free Quebec™ – $24.95
___ 838 Rifts® WB 23: Xiticix Invasion™ – $20.95
___ 839 Rifts® Coalition Wars®: Sedition™ – $20.95
___ 840 Rifts® Coalition Wars®: Coalition Overkill™ – $16.95
___ 841 Rifts® Coalition Wars®: Sorcerers' Revenge™ – $16.95
___ 842 Rifts® Coalition Wars®: Cyber-Knights™ – $16.95
___ 843 Rifts® Coalition Wars®: Shadows of Evil™ – $16.95
___ 844 Rifts® Coalition Wars®: Final Siege™ – $24.95
___ 845 Rifts® Game Master Guide™ – $26.95
___ 846 Rifts® Aftermath™ – $24.95
___ 847 Rifts® DB5: Anvil Galaxy™ – $20.95
___ 848 Rifts® Book of Magic™ – $26.95
___ 849 Rifts® Adventure Guide™ – $24.95
___ 850 Rifts® Bionics Sourcebook™ – $16.95
___ 851 Rifts® DB 6: Three Galaxies™ – $20.95
___ 852 Rifts® Dark Conversions™ – $24.95
___ 853 Rifts® Chi-Town 'Burbs™ – $9.95
___ 854 Rifts® The Tolkeen Crisis™ – $12.95
___ 855 Rifts® The Black Vault™ – $9.95
___ 856 Rifts® The Vanguard™ – $9.95
___ 857 Rifts® WB 24: China One™ – $20.95
___ 858 Rifts® WB 25: China Two™ – $20.95
___ 859 Rifts® DB 7: Megaverse Builder™ – $16.95
___ 860 Rifts® DB 8: Naruni Wave Two™ – $16.95
___ 862 Rifts® WB 26: Dinosaur Swamp™ – $20.95
___ 863 Rifts® MercTown™ – $20.95
___ 865 Rifts® Merc Ops™ – $20.95
___ 866 Rifts® WB 27: Adventures in Dinosaur Swamp™ – $20.95
___ 867 Rifts® Mercenary Adventure Sourcebook – $12.95
___ 868 Rifts® WB 28: Arzno™ – $20.95
___ 869 Rifts® WB 29: Madhaven™ – $16.95
___ 870 Rifts® John Zeleznik Coloring Book – $5.95
___ 871 Rifts® Machinations of Doom™ – $18.95
___ 872 Rifts® DB 10: Hades™ – $24.95
___ 873 Rifts® DB 11: Dyval™ – $24.95
___ 874 Rifts® WB 30: D-Bees of North America™ – $24.95
___ 875 Rifts® DB12: Dimensional Outbreak – $24.95

___ 876 Rifts® Megaverse® in Flames™ – $24.95
___ 876HC Rifts® Megaverse® in Flames™ Gold Hardcover Edition – $50.00
___ 877 Rifts® Heroes of the Megaverse® – $16.95
___ 878 Rifts® Sourcebook: Shemarrian Nation™ – $16.95
___ 880 Phase World®: Fleets of the Three Galaxies™ – $16.95
___ 881 Rifts® WB 31: Triax™ Two – $24.95
___ 883 Rifts® DB 14: Thundercloud Galaxy™ – $20.95
___ 884 Rifts® Vampires Sourcebook™ – $20.95
___ 885 Rifts® WB 32: Lemuria™ – $24.95
___ 886 Rifts® Black Market™ – $24.95
___ 886HC Rifts® Black Market™ Hardcover Gold Edition – SOLD OUT!
___ 887 Rifts® WB 33: Northern Gun™ One – $24.95
___ 888 Rifts® WB 34: Northern Gun™ Two – $26.95
___ 889 Rifts® Sourcebook: Coalition States, Heroes of Humanity™ – $20.95
___ 890 Rifts® World Book: Secrets of the Atlanteans™ – $24.95
___ 890HC Rifts® Secrets of the Atlanteans™ Hardcover Gold Edition – $50.00
___ 891 Rifts® World Book: Sovietski™ – $24.95
___ 892 Rifts® Sourcebook: The Disavowed™ – $16.95 (coming)
___ 893 Rifts® CS: Heroes of Humanity™ Arsenal Sourcebook – $16.95 (coming)
___ 894 Rifts® Haunted Tech™ – $16.95 (coming)
___ 895 Rifts® Living Nowhere™ – $16.95 (coming)
___ 896 Rifts® Bestiary™: North America, Volume One – $24.95 (coming)
___ 897 Rifts® Bestiary™: North America, Volume Two – $24.95 (coming)
___ 2510 Rifts® & The Megaverse® Art Book – $22.95
___ 2510-HC Rifts® & The Megaverse® Art Book, Hardcover – $50.00
___ 2510-CML Rifts® & The Megaverse® Art Book, Collector's Masterwork Edition – $125.00

Miscellaneous Products

___ 600 Deluxe Revised RECON® RPG – $22.95
___ 2537 Gamer Coffee Mug – $10.00
___ 2539 Rifts® Dice Bag – Black – $8.00
___ 2545 Dead Reign™ Coffee Mug – $10.00
___ 2554 Palladium Bookmarks, Set One – $5.00
___ 2555 Palladium Bookmarks, Set Two – $5.00
___ 2561 Property of Chi-Town Library Pencil – $0.50 each
___ 2562 Future Visions™ – The Artistry of Charles Walton II – $13.95
___ 2566 Glitter Boy Mouse Pad – $9.95
___ 2567 Old Ones Mouse Pad – $9.95
___ 2568 Zombie Graveyard Mouse Pad – $9.95
___ 2575 Rifts Poker Cards 1 (full color) – $11.99
___ 2576 Rifts Poker Cards 2 (line art) – $11.99

Note: T-shirts and other products can be found online: www.palladiumbooks.com

Rifts® Miniatures

___ MI8002 Xiticix Pack – $18.00
___ MI8004 Coalition Dog Pack – $18.00
___ MI8005 Men of Magic Pack #1 – $18.00
___ MI8006 Cyborgs Pack #1 – $18.00
___ MI8007 Simvan & Ostrosaurus Pack – $18.00
___ MI8008 Coalition Skelebots Pack #1 – $18.00
___ MI8009 Coalition SAMAS Pack #1 – $22.00
___ MI8010 Coalition Sky Cycle Pack – $22.00
___ MI8011 Coalition Dog Pack #2 – $18.00
___ MI8015 Damaged Skelebots Pack #1 – $12.00
___ MI8016 Cyber-Adventurers Pack – $18.00
___ MI8017 Rogues & Scout Pack #1 – $18.00
___ MI8018 Brodkil & Witchling Pack – $18.00
___ MI8019 Damaged Skelebots Pack #2 – $18.00
___ MI8020 Psi-Stalkers & Scouts Pack #1 – $18.00
___ MI8021 Shadow Beast – $12.00
___ MI8022 Mystic Knight – $6.00
___ MI8023 Lord Magus – $6.00
___ MI8026 Coalition Dog Boy in DPM-D1 Armor – $6.00
___ MI8027 Coalition Dog Boy #2 – $6.00
___ MI8028 Coalition Dog Boy #3 – $6.00
___ MI8029 Coalition Dog Boy #4 – $6.00
___ MI8030 Coalition Dog Boy #5 – $6.00
___ MI8033 Kydian Overlord – $20.00
___ MI8034 Dragonsaurus – $10.00
___ MI8035 Slaver and Slave (Atlantis) Set – $10.00
___ MI8036 Crazy – $6.00
___ MI8037 Juicer #1 – $6.00
___ MI8038 Juicer #2 – $6.00
___ MI8039 Cyborg #1 – $12.00
___ MI8040 Cyborg #2 – $12.00
___ MI8041 Cyborg #3 – $6.00
___ MI8042 Coalition Officer – $6.00
___ MI8044 Coalition Grunt #2 – $6.00
___ MI8045 Coalition Grunt #3 – $6.00

www.palladiumbooks.com

2018 Palladium Open House

- **100+ Palladium game events.**
- **Play games run by Kevin Siembieda & other Palladium creators.**
- **Participate in *panel talks* and many Q&A chats.**
- **Meet *Kevin Siembieda* and the Palladium staff.**
- **Meet *30+ Palladium creators*.**
- **Meet fellow gamers from around the world.**
- **Bring your favorite game books to get signed.**
- **Get autographs from all the Palladium creators.**
- **Get new releases, back stock items & Palladium collectibles.**
- **Get original artwork and limited edition prints.**
- **Price of admission pays for all events!**
- **Make memories to last a lifetime.**

The Palladium Open House is a rare event. The last one was held in 2015. It is limited to around 300 people, plus 30-50 Palladium creators and staff; the largest gathering of Palladium writers, artists and personalities anywhere in the world. And most make themselves available to you for 8-10 hours a day.

Sit down with Kevin Siembieda, the Palladium staff and our creators to talk and laugh about just almost anything. We've been told repeatedly by those who have attended past POHs that the atmosphere is more like a family reunion where they feel welcomed as friends. Our secret? We're gaming geeks like you, and we really are glad to see you. Whether you are someone we've come to know over the years and consider a friend, or a gamer we've never met before, we're happy to spend this special weekend of gaming with you, and talk about games, comic books, movies, writing, drawing, and just about anything else you'd want to chat about. And you do it all at the Palladium offices and warehouse, where the magic happens.

The price of admission covers ALL events and gives you access to all the guests, Kevin and crew, gaming events (first come, first served), panel talks, the auction and other activities. Come for one day or the whole weekend.

Three days of non-stop Palladium gaming, laughs and fun.

100+ Gaming Events – April 20-22, 2017:

- After the Bomb®	- Phase World®/Three Galaxies™
- Beyond the Supernatural™	- Rifts®
- Dead Reign®	- Rifts® Chaos Earth®
- Heroes Unlimited™	- Robotech®
- Nightbane®	- Robotech® RPG Tactics™
- Ninjas & Superspies™	- Splicers®
- Palladium Fantasy RPG®	- and more . . .

- **Plus open gaming, panel talks, and hanging out.**
- **Game with the people who make your favorite games and sourcebooks, like Kevin Siembieda, Julius Rosenstein, Carl Gleba, Carmen Bellaire, Brandon Aten, Greg Diaczyk, and others.**

- **ALL events, Friday thru Sunday, are covered under the price of admission.**
- **Meet 30+ Palladium creators – the largest gathering of Palladium creators in the world! Most available every day, the entire day.**
- **Live auction (Saturday evening) with rare, out of print books, original artwork, proofreader copies of manuscripts, collectibles, books from the Erick Wujcik collection, and more.**
- **Intimate setting. Easy access to Palladium creators.**
- **Held at the Palladium warehouse and offices.**
- **Doors open from 9:00 A.M. to 12:30 A.M. (possibly later).**
- **This is not a media event. It is a role-playing game event.** That mean ROLE-PLAYING GAMES for three days straight! (And for those of you who can make it, VIP Thursday too.)

Start planning NOW! As always, we plan to make the 2018 Palladium Open House fun and memorable, so order your admissions tickets and make your plans. Bring a friend and have the time of your life. And please tell other gamers about the 2018 POH.

"Confirmed" Palladium Creators, Artists, Writers & Personalities

- The Palladium Staff (Kevin, Wayne, Alex, Julius, Scott, and Kathy)
- Amy L. Ashbaugh (Artist)
- Brandon Aten (Writer; Triax 2, Madhaven, Sovietski, The Rifter®)
- Matthew Balent (Author of Weapons & Armor, Weapons & Castles, Monsters & Animals, and was present at the start of Palladium).
- Carmen Bellaire (Writer; Powers Unlimited® 1-3, Splicers®, RRT)
- Joe Bergmans (Honorary Staff Member & Consultant)
- James Brown (Game Master Supreme, Megaversal Ambassador)
- Steve Dawes (Writer; Dark Places and The Rifter®)

- Greg Diaczyk (Writer; Rifts® Lemuria and The Rifter®)
- Mark Dudley (Artist)
- Carl Gleba (Writer; Atlanteans, Megaverse in Flames, Three Galaxies, Minion War series, and others, and an awesome G.M.)
- Chris Guertin (Honorary Staff Member/Helper)
- Patrick "Jake" Jakubowski (Megaversal Ambassador & G.M.)
- Doug Lamberson (Honorary Staff Member/Helper)
- "Madman" Mike Leonard (Artist and Writer)
- Mike Mumah (Artist)
- Mark Oberle (Writer; Nightbane® Survival Guide, Dark Designs)
- Ben Rodriguez (Artist)
- Jeff "NMI" Ruiz (Palladium Online Administrator)
- Charles Walton (Artist)
- Taylor White (Writer/Musician; CE Resurrection, Hell Followed)
- John Zeleznik (Artist)
- And other Palladium personalities are anticipated.
- "Tentative" Ramon K. Perez (Artist, Comic Book Artist)
- "Tentative" Sean Patrick Fannon (Rifts® Savage Worlds) and others.

Price of Admission

Advance Ticket Purchase Guarantees Your Admission – April 20, 21 & 22, 2018 (VIP Night, April 19, 2018 is an additional day and an extra cost of $95).

- **3-Day Weekend Pass (Friday, Saturday & Sunday): $55** per person.
- **Friday (only): $30**
- **Saturday (only): $30**
- **Sunday (only; day ends at 5:00 PM): $12**
- **VIP Thursday (this is an ADDITIONAL cost): $95** (if you plan to attend the rest of the weekend you'll need to get a Weekend Pass too). VIP Thursday is limited to around 100 people plus the Palladium Staff and Freelancers. You get the delicious dinner, plus an extra afternoon and evening of gaming (door opens at 3:00 PM, dinner 6:00 PM), a more intimate chance to talk with Palladium staff, artists and writers, and get first crack at rare collectibles, prints and original art.

Note: As has become tradition, we hold 40 VIP slots to be offered in January so that gamers who decide to attend at a later date have a chance at getting into the coveted VIP Night too.

Methods of Payment

All major credit cards are accepted.

Online: Go to the Palladium online store at *www.palladiumbooks.com* to place your order the same as you would a book.

By Telephone: Call (734) 721-2903 – have your credit card information ready: Credit Card Number – name on the card – address of the credit cardholder – expiration Date – telephone number of the cardholder – code on the back of the card. Plus, your FULL address and apartment number, and the full NAME of *EACH person* you are ordering a ticket for.

By Mail: Send check or money order to:
Palladium Books – Dept. POH
39074 Webb Court
Westland, MI 48185-7606

Please include your FULL address and apartment number, and the full name of *each person* you are ordering a ticket for, and your telephone number in case there is a problem and we need to contact you.

All tickets are sold on a first come, first served basis, so get your reservations in as soon as possible! Due to space and parking limitations and safety concerns, attendance will be limited to approximately 300 admission tickets.

Cancellation: You can cancel your Open House or V.I.P. order up to March 1, 2018 and get a FULL refund. But please don't place an order unless you REALLY think you'll be able to attend.

Order early to guarantee your place at the 2018 Palladium Open House and to help us plan events. We NEED to know in advance how many gamers are coming so we have enough gaming events to keep everyone busy. The sooner you order, the better for Palladium. Credit Cards will be charged immediately.

All "advance" reservations must be in by *April 2, 2018.* A name must be assigned to EACH ticket you order. No refunds for cancellations after March 1, 2018. No refunds for no-shows.

Tickets will be available at the door, provided there is still room! **Kathy Simmons** will be handling reservations and tickets, so you know everything will be timely and organized.

Open House Hotels

Two hotels to choose from. Both are five minutes from the Palladium warehouse.

If you know you are coming, reserve your room NOW. The hotel does not charge your credit card till two days prior to the event and you can cancel up to a few days before. No risk. No cost to you now. And you guarantee your room. The number of double beds is limited.

- **Hampton Inn and Suites** – 734-844-1111 – Request the "POH" Group Rate. Free hot breakfast buffet and free wi-fi.
  - **$119.00 per night plus tax for "double Queen beds."**
  - **$129 per night for one "King Suite"** (one king bed and a pull out sofa).
- **Red Roof Inn Plymouth** – 734-459-3300 – Request the "Palladium Books Group Rate." Rooms sold on a first-come, first-served basis.
  - **$49.95 plus tax per night for a** *double* **(2 double beds).**
  - **$49.95 plus tax per night for a** *King* **(one large bed).**

See more complete details in the online store description.

Airport Note: The hotels and Palladium's warehouse are 15-20 minutes from *Detroit Metropolitan Airport (DTW)* in Romulus, Michigan, near I-275. Detroit Metro is the airport you want to use.

April (19), 20, 21 & 22, 2018 POH
Palladium Books – 39074 Webb Court – Westland, MI 48185
www.palladiumbooks.com

Gaming Through History

Optional Rules and Guidelines for All Palladium Games

By Hendrik Härterich

Many game lines of Palladium Books are set in our day and age. They lend themselves just as well to games set in any other time. I find it a fascinating and rewarding exercise to set my adventures in a different era.

Especially *Beyond the Supernatural™, Dead Reign®,* and *Nightbane®* get a new twist when they are set in the past. What about *Flashing Blades of Horror* (BtS in the Elizabethan and Stuart age), *Nightbane by Gaslight* (when the Nightlords assault Her Britannic Majesty's Victorian Empire), or *Civil War Apocalypse* (Dead Reign 1861-1865)? I particularly love playing *Hard Boiled Horror* (BtS Noir in the 1930s) and had roaring BtS adventures set in the 2nd World War for *Eerie Company 194x.*

A G.M. may shy away from using the vast richness of our past as it seems to be a lot of work to "create" the setting. It can be but it does not have to be. This article will help you on your way to gaming through history and to define your historical era game.

While this article is geared toward *Beyond the Supernatural™,* the thoughts and techniques laid out herein will aid you in creating an era game for any Palladium game line.

Frame

Inspiration source: You will probably start to develop your idea when reading a history novel or watching a costume drama. Who has not been inspired for his fantasy role-playing game when watching – or for gamers I should probably say: studying – any of the Robin Hood movies or when reading Ivanhoe? Hold that thought. It is your first glimpse through the keyhole to a wonderful new gaming world and it will keep you motivated. Write down what you liked about this inspiration source. What grabbed you? What was exciting? As important: which parts didn't you like?

How exact do you need to be: Always remember, it is a game, not a history simulation, unless the latter is what floats your and your party's boat. You can allow yourself to be liberal with respect to historical exactitude. There is no rule that says there cannot be airships in the Three Musketeers. I know, not in history and not in Alexandre Dumas' awesome book, but it worked rather nicely in The Three Musketeers (2011) with Christoph Waltz, Ray Stevenson, and Orlando Bloom. If you want to be exact, you will be facing a fascinating history research project. I love doing that, but I have found out that not all players share my love for detail and that much of my research was for "nothing" as it found no use in my game. As always, know your party. They are your people, your audience, and what is more: your buddies. You do not want to bore them. Heck, even Shakespeare was taking a lot of historical liberties. So can you! Do what you need to do to *make the era game credible and always fun. It is all about verisimilitude*, not about building the perfect era cage. Let the game breathe!

Brainstorming: Let us use that first motivational boost to jot down the frame for the game. When you think about the era, what comes to your mind? What are your and the general era preconceptions – be those from your history lessons, from a documentary, or even pop culture references? In my experience, the way history is shown in movies, TV series, comic books, etc. is perhaps the best source for your game. It is what every geek knows. It will make your game seep quickly into your players' minds. A good writer will not describe every single detail, he will leave room for the reader to fill the gaps with his own imagination. You can use that. In fact, you should. A good G.M. does not need to describe every square inch but lets the players draw most of the picture by themselves. For example, just saying that the NPC looks much like Humphrey Bogart in Casablanca will create an instant picture in your players' minds. We will come back to this later, but keep in mind, your era game will have the basic stage set already when you do just enough to kick your players' imagination into gear, and that is easiest when you play up to "what everyone knows" or when you can reference a movie you all have seen. Well, be that as it may, you also need to think about populating your world. Who are the VIPs of the era, who comes to your mind? It can be very cool for the players to meet historical persons, be they real or fictitious. Who would not love to talk to Sherlock Holmes, solve the Jack the Ripper mystery, and be rewarded with a knighthood by Queen Victoria for your troubles? And then there is the general scene and what I call the background chatter. What are, roughly, the main events? What was the biggest hype of the time? Are there some new-fangled inventions, like the car or electricity, which change the world at the moment of your game? Do such innovations play a role in your game? What shocked everyone in the newspapers of the day? Is there a Hindenburg disaster or something similar that will be talked about for months? Chances are if you know it today without having to think much about it, it was probably a big event. Write all that down. You will test and refine the results of your brainstorming, but the likelihood is you have just taken 30 minutes or even less and put down the cornerstones of your setting.

Reduce to grow: Now, you will probably start digging into the era. The Internet has made that easy. Wikipedia is a great starting point and will often give you enough information to go along with, but you may want to read on. Googling era pictures gives you a pretty good impression quickly but will also flood you with images. There is a humongous amount of information out there, a lot of it at your fingertips. In fact, one of the hardest jobs you have now is to reduce. You have to **fo-**cus on an era – decade – country – area**, like San Francisco, USA, 1930s. Start in one city or, at least, elect an era/area like "starts on the US West Coast between the two Great Wars." If you do not do that you will quickly be overwhelmed. We have to avoid that. It would quench your appetite for your game needlessly and just give you lots of information you will, in all probability, not need later on.

Immersion

Immerse yourself in era-contemporary culture: Next you want to get into the groove. A great starting point is listening to the soundtrack of the movie that has inspired you. Or, achieving the next level of immersion, you might want to listen to actual era pieces. As with all the research I have done for my games I have discovered a lot of stuff I did not know before and that is a rather enriching side effect. Era pieces and movie soundtracks are inspiring. You cannot quite beat listening to any Indiana Jones soundtrack, or "Lili Marleen" and "White Cliffs of Dover" when preparing a 2nd World War BtS action-heist adventure. Likewise, watching original newsreels, listening to old radio broadcasts, or perhaps even reading correspondence/letters from the time will give you real information on an era scoop as well as get you closer to the style of presentation, points of reference, and even manners. It is too easy to get lost here, again. Go as deep as you like to – creating is supposed to be fun, too! – but do not lose your focus: you have a job to do and put meat on the bones of your basic framework. Immersion has two functions. First, it helps you to get a better feel for the setting – it will become more "real" to you. Second, it will help you later to set the scene with a truer "feel." Some players will enjoy getting a link or two, e.g. for era music or a typical picture, before the game itself starts. Who says marketing is only for business, eh? A word of caution, though: do not flood your players with information; it may quench their thirst. That said, an iconic music piece may become the theme song of your game and you may elect to play it at the start of each session. Also, you may even draw adventure ideas from broadcasts, etc.

Choose the premise of your first adventure, choose places, and the exact time: In order to focus your attention even more, you can now opt to concentrate your work further. The era is the backdrop, the stage if you will. You may want to decide on your first adventure now. No matter how handsomely you are able to capture the zeitgeist of your chosen era, what will grab your players by the throat is not all the fluff around them or your historical expertise, but the actual adventure they will play on the stage you are setting. As with all good shows, there should be interdependency of stage and play. So, in order to set that stage right, you need to decide what the players will experience. This will also go a long way to bring order to the informational clutter you have unearthed so far and show you where it will be worthwhile for the adventure to dig deeper. So, what will happen to the players? What will they see, where will they go? What is the basic premise of the game? How would you describe your game idea if you had only 30 seconds to do it, i.e. *what is your elevator pitch? Write it down.*

For example, you have decided to let your players *parachute into Axis occupied Crete in mid 1941 to fight the supernatural* (your elevator pitch) as your first adventure. When you thought about 1941, you would, of course, have remembered or stumbled over the Attack on Pearl Harbor. While the latter is extremely interesting, what happened in the Pacific theater in December 1941 really has no impact at all on the situation in Greece in May of the same year. Pearl Harbor is too far away and the attack actually "has not happened yet" when seen from Greece in May 1941. You can see from that example, that by deciding where and when exactly (month now) the adventure will play, you can strike off a lot of the information "assaulting" you, which refers to events either after the date of your adventure or about elsewhere. You want to specify the year and month when the game will take place as well as the general, or if possible, specific locations of your adventure. Specifying what your adventure is about will also guide you to the information you really need.

Research what you need, identify icons: Does the party need transport? If so, you might want to look up plane or vehicle types or train connections and train fares. Does your party need weapons? Of course they will (hah, hah), so a nice spot of research is identifying what the iconic weapons of the era are. Depending on the time available to you and how passionate you are about historical research, this part can take quite a while. It does not have to, though. I dare say, if you devote a few hours on some core topics you will get an optimal output with a bearable input. By all means, do not let this distract you from writing your Ph.D. but for your game, in all probability, all you need is to *identify what the iconic set-pieces and tools are and give them basic research*. When you set your adventure in the Shanghai of 1937, you do not need to learn Mandarin or create a 3D model of the city at the time to make the setting credible to your players. However, you really want to have a look at a city map of Shanghai of that time, get a good idea of the basic layout of the city quarters, read up a little of the history of that year, decide if your adventure will be before or after the Battle for Shanghai or incorporate those events, and find the iconic images and tropes for era & area. For example, a Shanghai nightclub (like Club Obi Wan in "Temple of Doom"), a wise, old Chinese gentlemen as an NPC, putting in some sights – like a walk on The Bund, a teahouse, an opium den, a trip with a junk – enemies using martial arts and old swords like Japanese soldiers or Chinese tong members, corrupt but suave French policemen (echo of "Casablanca"), tommy guns, etc., would all be fair choices as icons in your game. In short, using icons – **iconic places, tropes, and stereotypes** – also makes quick identification of the players with the setting possible. They will recognize and respond to the icons and find their way around more easily. Remember always, though, do not bite off more than you can or need to chew. It does not make any sense to devote days on a subject that you will not need

to research for your game. Sure, you can read whole books on firearms in the 18th Century, but doing so may make you lose your focus for your game and setting. The setting is not in a gun, the gun is just one tool of many within your game. The likelihood is that you will need to know only the basics for your "Tea Party of Death" zombie game, after all.

Using Stereotypes: Stereotypes are a very valuable tool for quick player immersion, but do not overdo them. It is perfectly ok to have all Nazi soldiers in your game like sauerkraut, throw snappy salutes, wear extremely crisp uniforms, and be fanatically loyal to the Third Reich, perhaps even to speak with "ze horrible akzent," but if all soldiers of the Evil Empire are stupid like lobotomized mules or miss all the time, the enemy is hard to take seriously. Always go by the old adage: *the good ones go into the pot, the bad ones go into your crop!* You want to employ stereotypes only to improve and ease recognition by the players – e.g. a BtS adventure in the age of rapiers *needs* dashing fencers and Errol Flynn-style sword fights, and Hardboiled Horror without a tough private eye and fedoras would be strange, but you do not want to create cardboard villains. Do not confuse iconic elements and era tropes with cardboard laughing stock and devote some time to deciding which are helpful and which would be harmful. That said, even a caricature has value as comic relief, but do not let more than one of the stereotypes you use degrade into caricature or you will lose the credibility of your setting. A character like Sergeant Hans Schultz can provide comic relief and even inadvertent help to the players, but if you use more than that you might as well play a "Hogan's Heroes" game straight away. A good test is to imagine the comic relief character in a serious movie. Would he destroy the flair of danger and adventure or help it along? I for one have a hard time seeing Schultz in "Guns of Navarone" or "Band of Brothers" at all, so if the tone is gritty, comic relief is probably misplaced. A second test is what I call the Binks Test. A bad way to introduce comic relief: Jar Jar Binks in the Star Wars prequels. A good way to do it: C3PO in the classic Star Wars.

Boldly go where others have gone before: Great minds think alike and all that. There is a fair chance that you are not the first person on Earth to create a (horror or adventure) story in a different era. I can only recommend to look out for novels and movies playing in the "your" era and with a similar gist. What-if novels or stories actually written in your chosen era, especially when they fit your genre, can be a great inspiration to give your setting an additional spin. Allow yourself to be inspired. Even when badly done, the works of others can be good for you as you can learn how you do *not* want to do it.

Ask for advice: Aside from using the strange powers of the interwebs or your home library, use your public libraries and ask a librarian for advice. If you mention an era to a librarian, or to the guy at the bookstore, and say what you are researching or which kind of genre/novel type you want, they will often surprise you with some neat advice. Also, the friendly people on the Forums of the Megaverse will always help a fellow gamer.

Adapting the Rules to the Setting

Weapons and Armor: You have already identified the iconic weapons of the era. You need to be sure that you have statted them out as well. This is fairly easy. Between Palladium Fantasy and Dead Reign/BtS, you have a pretty long list of ancient to modern weapons, from melée to ranged and including a fair number of firearms. Still, when a weapon is iconic – like a musket, Tommy gun or rapier – you want to be extra sure that you do not only have a close analogue at hand but write down the particulars, including changing any existing stats to your personal taste. Simple tricks can go a long way to change the game. For example, when you double all damage ratings in the book, your game will become more deadly straight away; maybe that is what you need for your *The Dirty Dozen against the Nightlords* adventure. If you have the book or can get it, "Transdimensional TMNT" was an excellent supplement and has weapons through the ages covered excellently and absolutely compatible with today's S.D.C. games. In any case, though, brace yourself for some discussions with some players on whatever you decide in terms of arms & armor, but getting down the details for iconic arms & armor will go a long way to make most players happy.

Money, Purchasing Power, Equipment: There are three basic options I would suggest for your choice. Choose a solution YOU are comfortable with and that works for your game.

The simple choice: You can make use of existing equipment lists from the various Palladium games, of course; there is a ready price tag to be found for a great variety of items. However, Palladium Fantasy uses "gold" and "silver" and BtS, Dead Reign, etc. use prices fitting for our day and age. Now, one can downplay purchasing of any sort or simply use today's prices, of course, but in my experience different currencies and values add a lot of flavor to the game. Perhaps you simply spice the existing lists up by calling the coinage used Louis D'Or or Ecu and pistols – by the way, a pistol was the French penny and that is actually where the term for the short firearm came from as they shot "pistol"-sized ammunition – or pounds and pennies. Well, and then it is also a valuable and simple option to just check out other role-playing supplements and fan sites; perhaps somebody somewhere has already made an equipment list for your era.

The research option: Yet, these simpler solutions may not satisfy you and, be assured, you can dig much deeper. It is not so difficult to find out the approximate (a) value relationship between currencies in your setting and (b) the purchasing power ratio between then and now, at least when the game is set after 1900. The information is accessible online through government statistics, which seriously started not much before that. However, it is more difficult when the game is set before the modern age; middle ages and renaissance information on prices etc. is available but not as readily as for the 20th Century. Even when going to a university library and researching historical texts, the information tends not to be in one place. It can also be confusing. For example, the Holy Roman Empire of German Nation alone had about 200 individual currencies around the time of the 30 Years War. Now, if you have an in-terest in the history of economy or numismatics, by all means dig away, but for most of us, it is probably simpler to make a creative judgment call and go back to the above idea to simply rename the Dollar or Gold Coin currency. As you can see, this will not lead to a quick result, but we can make your work easier.

The nifty option: Use ratios! A real gem of a currency converter which I warmly recommend is to be found at **https://www.measuringworth.com/ppoweruk/** with the help of which you may convert English coins from as early as 1270 to the equivalent value of today. Not far from that calculator is the same converter service for the US from money as far back as 1774 ready to convert into today's currency and loads of other intriguing historical-economic information. For the converter result, I strongly suggest to use the "real price" / "historic standard of living" and to round up the result for easy in-game calculation. Whether or not there is a similar service for other currencies/countries, it should not be too difficult to find the relative worth of other currencies to e.g. of the Spanish ducat to the English pound of 1588 (Armada hint: the ducat totally plummeted after that year). For example, in the 1930s, one US Dollar had the average purchasing power of about 15 bucks today (ratio of $1 USD in 2016 to $17.40 USD in 1932). There is a difference between "real value," "income value," "labor value," etc. but, unless you are a buff and love getting your brain into a happy knot over economic development, I suggest to keep it simple with one ratio and work from there. You will already have reached a pretty high level of relative accuracy. Simply googling 1930s, or whatever year/age you want to play in, salaries will give you a good idea of what people earned at the time (1932: on average, 150 USD per month, etc.). A little further research will give you an idea of prices for housing, cost to buy a vehicle, train fares, etc. Even if you do not want to do the latter yet more detailed research you should already be fine when you just use the existing equipment and price lists with the ratio you found.

One final word on money and goods/services: While directly converting is fine, as suggested above, remember that scarce goods (supply & demand) or cutting edge products will cost more. A watch was a very luxurious piece of equipment in the 16th Century, for example. For convenience, multiply today's prices by 10-100 for very rare or cutting edge products, less for just reasonably scarce goods, and use a snappy version of the product as the calculation basis – use an expensive watch (e.g. costing 10,000 USD), use a high multiplier (x100), and then apply the ratio (320). Your Rollodeaf watch would then cost a staggering £ 3,150 in Elizabethan England, and obviously even more for the bejeweled version – a nobleman's annual income.

Core Flair Rule: For some settings you may need to adapt the rules further. In BtS, a very simple but genius rule – "Proximity to the Supernatural" – expresses the whole idea of the setting and explains why those fighting the supernatural are pretty powerless without the supernatural around them. It explains why using spells or psionics is not a business-as-usual thing or something that is seen every day. Such a rule is what I dub a "core flair rule" and one which you want to keep for any

BtS game. At the same time, you may need to create an additional core flair rule typical and expressing something special or iconic for your setting. For example, Flashing Blades of Horror will work perfectly fine without any new rules on fencing, but as it is so focal for the setting – a musketeer movie without fencing or fencing stunts is simply inconceivable and would certainly be bland – you might want to tune the rules to that. Here, searching *The Rifter*® is often helpful. Fencing, for example, has received a fair treatment in "Flashing Blades – Fencing in Palladium Fantasy" in *The Rifter*® #22 (pages 62-67), which you may use directly or use as a leg up to make your own rule.

Occupations, O.C.C.s/P.C.C.s, and Skills: You do not necessarily need new P.C.C.s or O.C.C.s. Actually, in my experience, that is not necessary at all no matter in what era you play. The existing BtS P.C.C.s/O.C.C.s are more than sufficient to cover every angle (well, almost, as long as there is no Arcanist in BtS-II). However, what you will definitely benefit from are new occupations.

Occupations are not only nifty, they focus and personalize your P.C.C./O.C.C. In an era game, **occupations are also a great means to convey the setting flair**. While I strongly recommend creating at least a few new occupations iconic to the era, if a G.M. wants to avoid making up new occupations, you can use the existing occupations by adapting them to your era. Dead Reign and BtS occupations can be used for both games – Dead Reign copies most of the BtS occupations but has some new ones as well. **Use common sense to adapt the existing occupations and skills**. Not all skills make sense for an era game; for example: Aircraft Mechanics makes no sense at all in Elizabethan England and would need to be struck, of course. Just go through the skill list and strike what does not fit. If an occupation loses skills that way, put in what fits for the era or give more free picks. Also, check whether you need or want to adapt the Common Skills. In my 1930s Hardboiled Horror game, for example, I made W.P. Rifle and Military Etiquette Common Skills provided the character had a background of having been a soldier in the first World War.

That said, if you go about making up new occupations, you will probably want to know how many skills, etc. you should allocate. BtS-II occupations allocate 8-16 Occupational Skills with a bonus ranging from +4 to +30%. Both the lowest and the highest bonuses are very rare. The Occupational Skills bonus total ranges from 35 to 215 – again, with the lowest and the highest sum being exceedingly rare. The low end results from the occupation (in this case: Athletics: Fighting Competitor) having a lot of Physical skills without a percentile value and only a few "normal" skills. Not all occupations start with Hand to Hand or W.P. skills – these usually have to be taken separately as Elective Skills. Occupations give 6-10 elective skills with a bonus range from 5-15 and 2-6 Secondary Skills. About half of the occupations do not add further Secondary Skills, the others have a wide range of different level steps (add one Secondary Skill at levels 5 and 10 or at levels 3, 6, 9, and 12, for example) – a good average is to add one Secondary Skill every 4 levels, i.e. at levels 4, 8, and 12.

Rule of thumb to create a new occupation: A new occupation has around 12 Occupational Skills; the usual bonus for most of these will be +15%, but maybe as low as +5% or as high as +30% (very rare). In order to check whether you are overdoing it on the bonus side for the Occupational Skills, the "checksum" – i.e., when adding all bonuses of the Occupational Skills – is 140%. The new occupation should have about 7 Elective Skills (but you can go as low as 4 and as high as 8), with a bonus of 10% each, but you should restrict the bonus to certain skill groups. The standard is to give a bonus of +10% for skills chosen from the standard available categories (see BtS-II, page 173) plus one or maximum two other areas normally not available (BtS-II, page 173) as Elective Skills, such as Rogue or Espionage skills. Further, allow for about 4 Secondary Skills from the standard available categories at level one, +1 additional skill at levels 3, 6, 9, and 12.

Physical occupations, like soldiers, policemen, or sportsmen, will have 5 Physical skills, including one Hand to Hand and some Weapon Proficiencies fitting for the occupation. *Scholarly occupations*, like teachers, technicians, lawyers, etc., will start without Hand to Hand or W.P. skills, unless they take them up electively. *Hardy types*, like rogues, tough handymen, traveling craftsmen, and investigators, will have 1 or 2 Physical skills, which will firstly be a W.P. and may or may not be a Hand to Hand skill. *Everyone* can, of course, take Physical skills in general, and W.P. or Hand to Hand by spending Elective or even Secondary Skills.

Many occupations also have a Special Bonus. That should either be a skill bonus of +10% on any one skill from one to three skill groups or could be something very special like a bonus on strike +2 for a dedicated physical/warrior occupation. Be creative, the Special Bonus helps to highlight something about the occupation, but do not overpower it and err on the side of caution.

Setting Frame Sheet

You do not want to lose all your precious work and it never hurts to write down the basics. For this purpose I have created a one page setting frame sheet. When you do the brainstorming recommended above, this may be useful. It is handy and short – it summarizes your frame and the basic premise or your era game at a glance.

Getting Started, Sharing the Workload

You do not need to know all: A common mistake is the never-ending preparation. Research is all great fun but it has no point if you never start the game. The rule of thumb is to know enough to tell the story but not so much that you feel like giving a lesson or a history exam.

Involve the Players: In a regular game, your players will play their characters for many gamedays. They will become invested in their characters. A simple trick has been a great success for my group. *Firstly*, on character creation I tell the players the basic premise of the game (era, area, months and

SETTING FRAME SHEET

Catchy Title

Inspiration *(movie, book,...)*

Elevator Pitch *(based on which Palladium rules set? why is it exciting? what is it about? what is the cool part?)*

ICONS

Places:

Stereotypes:

VIPs:

Shockers of the Day:

Tech Innovations:

Typical Weapons:

ERA *(century, decade, reference name/period?)*

Era Classification *(what makes it?)*

CORE FLAIR RULES

Mood Pieces *(art, pictures, movies, radio broadcasts, music? what represents the era?)*

FOCUS
country/area:
decade/year:
special
event:

ToDos

MY FIRST ADVENTURE *(how to showcase the era best? how to make the introduction to this time?)*

year, and so forth) and give them a choice. Either I give them a dozen stereotypes to choose from or let them do their own character background. I attach only two rules to the latter: (i) the G.M. has the last word. Some players will make up a background that gives them too many contacts, too much money, etc. Players seek advantages and that is ok, but the G.M. has the right to curtail that and should when it imperils the bal-

ance he seeks for his game. Encourage the players to mix the good with the bad. Give them leeway to create a maximum number, say 1-3, contacts, if at all. (ii) The character must fit the basic premise. *Secondly*, during the game, I encourage the players to do their own research. If a player can show me that a certain event occurred, a certain person existed, some particular special equipment was available, etc. in "real history" and relevant to the players / the game, I will certainly take it into consideration. To a certain extent that allows the players to take part in shaping the world. This has worked wonderfully for my games and has enriched the setting and the adventure experience. If you allow your players to gain small advantages with their research, they will have extra incentive to immerse themselves in the world and research.

Flashing Blades of Horror

Beyond the Supernatural™ in the Swashbuckling Age

By Hendrik Härterich

Welcome to the age of flashing blades and dashing heroes! It is roughly the time between 1500-1700 A.D. – from the renaissance to the baroque or Tudors to Stuarts. Think Sir Francis Drake, Shakespeare, and the Three Musketeers and you are square in the middle of this age. This article will give you the framework to play Beyond the Supernatural in this glorious era, but it can be easily adapted to **Dead Reign®**, **Nightbane®**, or, indeed, any other Palladium game line.

Elevator Pitch

It is an age of scintillating wit and ready violence, where fortunes can be made by anyone with courage and luck, and where fate may well be decided on the tip of a sword or by the scratch of a pen. Ever wanted to be one of the Three Musketeers or brave the seven seas and the Spanish Armada like Sir Francis Drake? Well, then: Buckle your swash and prepare for adventure!

Historical Backdrop

The period chosen for this era game ranges from the time of the renaissance to the baroque. It is the age of muskets and blunderbusses, swashbuckling heroes like the musketeers, and a Europe catapulted forward on the wings of great inventions and tantalizing art.

It is an age of art, invention. Michelangelo paints the ceiling of the Sistine Chapel, true renaissance men like Leonardo da Vinci astound the people – just have a look at his fabulous notebooks – and England starts its ascent to imperial glory. The arts flourish. New musical instruments are developed, compositions become more complex and diverse. The greatest English writer since Chaucer appears on the world's stage: Shakespeare. He might have been a singularity but he was anything but alone; the reign of Elizabeth I saw a rare bloom of talent and the stages were set abuzz with new plays and delighted applause. The new world is (re)discovered. Sir Walter Raleigh is searching for El Dorado.

It is an age of conflict. The great powers of Europe are at war, not always but often. Piracy is licensed by kings to supplement their navy's power and fatten their coffers. Sir Francis Drake and his brethren roam the seas, usually hunting for Spanish gold.

The 16th Century sees wars for power, land grabbing and gold, but also the rise of a spiritual austerity and the will to recreate the Catholic Church. When Martin Luther nailed his 95 theses to the door of All Saints' Church in Wittenberg on 31 October 1517, he sparked the Reformation. Wise men had brilliant ideas and the works of Erasmus, Luther, Thomas More, Melanchton, Tyndale, Calvin, etc. set free a spirit that simply could not be bottled again. The church had not taken well to dissenting opinion before, there had been more Crusades against heretics within Europe than against heathens outside – like the Hussite War or the Albigensian Crusade against the Cathars – and it did not take well to some priests' and philosophers' ideas of reformation now. The result was persecution and violence but also freedom of thought, where the individual started to count in a way the common man had not counted since antiquity. The free everyman can become a hero!

It is a time of grand power plays. The violent fires of religious fervor burnt high in those times and made for an explosive mix with the rampant intrigues and power plays between and at the courts of Europe. France had the Huguenot Wars (also called the French Wars of Religion; 1562-1598) with the St. Bartholomew's Day Massacre (1572) which was ended by the Edict of Nantes.

The 5-year reign of Elizabeth's sister, Mary I (reign 1553-1558) did not give Mary the nickname "Bloody Mary" for nothing. In her reign Protestants were persecuted and executed. Elizabeth pacified England, true, but in her time, Catholics were persecuted as they tended to side with the Pope and Spain and thus against the interests of the crown. Being a Catholic meant to be close to be automatically considered a traitor. Many rich Catholics had secret rooms built into their houses to harbor fleeing priests, but woe to them and those they gave sanctuary when discovered. The Gunpowder plot of the Catholic extremist Guy Fawkes in the early reign of James I in 1605 almost became a very resonating echo of the explosive relationship between Protestants and Catholics in England.

Power, greed, and religious persuasion often could not be separated. Religious conviction and the will to rule England went hand in hand when His Most Catholic Majesty Philip II of Spain, brother in law to Elizabeth I, decided to invade England and sent the Spanish Armada to conquer in 1588. His plans were foiled, not least by the swashbuckling deeds of Francis Drake and John Hawkins. Do not be misled, this was but the largest engagement in the undeclared Spanish-English War of 1585-1604. There was ample opportunity for adventure!

There was, at best, an uneasy peace between England and France at most times. James I of England, first Stuart king, called himself also King of France as he did have a claim through their family line. One might think that was over with the end of the Hundred Years' War. Not so. There was a tangible and real threat to the French crown with every single royal English proclamation.

It is an age of espionage. Poison, meetings in the dark, and cloak and dagger are all ever present. Sir Francis Walsingham must have been one of the greatest spymasters in history and served his Queen, Elizabeth I, well. The playwright, Christopher Marlowe was supposed to be one of the crown's spies. Yet, not only Gloriana had access to a great spy network. France and Louis XIII later had their Cardinal Richelieu and his uncanny talent for spycraft which was just as legendary.

The 17th Century was no less shaken by religious conflict. Catholic Cardinals effectively co-ruled France – Mazarin and the already mentioned multifaceted and most fascinating Richelieu. The great kings of Spain, such as Charles V or Philip III, were not called "most Catholic Majesty" for nothing. The middle of Europe was set ablaze by the Thirty Years' War (1618-1648), while France to the west fortified its power and only dabbled in the great struggle to its east. The Holy Roman Empire of the German nation became one of the most terrible battlegrounds history has ever seen; two generations knew almost nothing but war – it must have felt like the coming of the riders of the apocalypse was imminent. England saw its Protestant Roundheads and noble Cavaliers do battle in the English Civil War (1642-1651) and had its Glorious Revolution (1688). Parliamentary power did not rise everywhere. Louis XIV was aptly called an absolute monarch and the Sun King, and he held himself to be the State by saying "L'etat ce moi!" He reigned for 72 years (1643-1715) and his reign saw a change of the power structure and economy of Europe.

It is a time of opportunity for the "new men" to climb far beyond their station at birth. There is a stark contrast between the upper class – the grandiose splendor of the courts and the glittering fortune and colorful fashion of the nobility – and the fate of most of the people. The age of flashing blades did see a firm divide between those of gentle birth and commoners; farmers mostly lived in bondage. Yet, a middle class is growing and the landed gentry and craftsmen and merchants

SETTING FRAME SHEET

Catchy Title
Flashing Blades of Horror

Inspiration *(movie, book,...)*
3 Musketeers, Elizabeth, Walsingham, Cloak & Dagger, Shakespeare

Elevator Pitch *(based on which Palladium rules set? why is it exciting? what is it about? what is the cool part?)* Age of scintillating wit & ready violence. Fortunes can be made by anyone with courage and luck. Fate will be decided on the tip of a sword or by the scratch of a pen. Buckle your swash!

ICONS

Places: England, France

Stereotypes:
D'Artagnan, Drake, Marlowe

VIPs: see above & Richelieu

Shockers of the Day: Spanish Armada, Plague

Tech Innovations: Drama, Black Powder wpns

Typical Weapons: Rapier, musket, pistol, pike, canon

ERA *(century, decade, reference name/period?)* 1500-1700

Era Classification *(what makes it?)* age of discovery, art boom

CORE FLAIR RULES

· Swashbuckling stunts and antics! If really necessary expand combat system.
· Black Powder Weapons! Introduce muskets, etc. to BtS
· Perhaps special "Stunt Rule"
· Modify "x1" Proximity to the Supernatural as people believe in "magic"

Mood Pieces *(art, pictures, movies, radio broadcasts, music? what represents the era?)* Watch any of the many Three Musketeer movies, TV series Flashing Blade, Elizabeth (both parts), Alatriste, Captain Kidd, Red Corsair; read Prisoner of Zenda; read on the lives of Christopher Marlowe, Caravaggio, Sir Francis Walsingham, Richelieu; listen to Anthony Holborne and John Dowland

FOCUS
country/area: England, France
decade/year: Around 1588 or 1620
special event: Lots - plots vs. crown

ToDos
Read Ian Mortimer's "The Time Traveller's Guide to Elizabethan England". CHECK OCCUPATIONS!

MY FIRST ADVENTURE *(how to showcase the era best? how to make the introduction to this time?)* Hook: Party is pressed into service for Walsingham to contact a spy in Calais (1585 game) or for Richelieu a French spy in La Rochelle (1625 game) on plot. Line: Spy has been murdered horribly. His papers are gone. Sinker: Last contact was a group of actors. One of the actors is a cultist.
Cult plans to get Queen/King's blood to summon a demon lord with it.

of the cities start making a deep and lasting mark on the social landscape, often achieving influence and position far beyond what their medieval forbears could even have dreamed of. For example, in England the somewhat personally motivated reformation by Henry VIII changed the political landscape and made him and his favorites rich by the forcible secularization of Catholic Church property – especially the so-called dissolution by seizure of monastic real estate. This is the reason why some of the landed gentry in the Elizabethan age lived in monasteries turned into manor houses. The rapid pace of discoveries, inventions, new ideas, and the ever present great equalizer – war – made a lot of room to advance oneself, some jumping from common birth up to the high ranks of nobility. Mayhap climbing the social ladder to fame and fortune is an aim for our heroes as well.

It is an age of literature, poetry, and great thought. Shakespeare, Spenser, Bacon, Ben Jonson, Thomas Kyd, and the adventurous Christopher (Kit) Marlowe – just to name a few – enriched the Elizabethan age and humanity with their verses. Playwrights and other artists were not some peace-loving hippie rhymers, but deeply embroiled in the intrigues and adventures of the day, drinking deeply from the cup of life. Cyrano de Bergerac, at least as literature has him, could fence one hundred men and make a witty couplet whilst doing it. Christopher Marlowe was probably a spy for Walsingham, and one very persistent legend has him dying in a staged bar room brawl. The painter Caravaggio, at a time the toast of Rome, was a fugitive murderer and notorious brawler, even in a time when brawling and duels were commonplace.

It is a time of larger than life characters, and the invented are not any stranger than those who really existed. YOU will decide who is real: the spy and assassin Captain Arturo Quire, the upright firebrand from the country D'Artagnan, the poet and master fencer Cyrano de Bergerac, the corsair and naval hero Sir Francis Drake, the New World adventurer Sir Walter Raleigh in search for the city of gold, the honorable sword for hire Capitano Alatriste, just to name a few.

Now, you gentles, allow your humble guide to show you the means to combat the supernatural in the dark alleys and hidden causeways of this colorful era where ghoulies and ghosties and long-legged beasties go bump in the night and flashing blades will clash!

Recommended Eras

- Elizabethan England (around the year 1588)
- Richelieu France (1622-1630)
- Stuart England to English Civil War (1603-1649)
- Conquistadors (1520-1530)
- Spanish Main (around 1650)

The Supernatural in the Age of Flashing Blades

People in the 16th and 17th Century, by and large, believe in magic and the supernatural. As magic and the supernatural are actually real in our game, this is not such an unenlightened attitude. In some countries, "witches" are burnt at the stake or drowned in those days, and magic is often seen as devilry by Catholics and Puritans alike. Thus, any display of "magic" might have very negative consequences, like a witch trial (Salem in the Colonies, for example) or impromptu lynching by a mob with pitchforks. The Stuart, King James I of England, actually not only commissioned the King James Bible version but wrote a book on devilry, magic, spirits and specters, including deliberations on possessions and obsessions ("*Daemonologie, In Forme of a Dialogue, Divided into Three Books,*" by the High and Mighty Prince, James etc., London 1597). Interestingly, for a BtS game he mentioned Succubae and Incubi as obsessions, i.e. spirits who trouble Man from the outside, and possessions as spirits assaulting Man from the inside. Most Entities in the BtS-II core book would fall into the latter category while the Dar'ota would squarely be in the "obsession" category.

That said, not everywhere and at all times was magic seen as evil. Let us not be fooled by prejudice and fears that, for a good part, evolved later. In the England of Queen Elizabeth I, witchcraft and sorcery were "only" punishable by hanging, not burning, and only if the use of magic had led to death. Essentially, magic was seen as a means only, not an offense per se. Hermetical scholars like the enigmatic Dr. John Dee even became counsel to royalty, Elizabeth I of England in that case, or (in)famous healers and seers like the peculiar Nostradamus. The Swiss alchemist Paracelsus searched for the Philosopher's Stone in earnest, like so many before him, and the well-known Sir Isaac Newton wrote more on alchemy than on anything else.

The 16th and 17th Century people were subjected to the very real horrors of war and plague, famine and poverty. The people – highborn and lowborn, educated and simple alike – were looking to the heavens for signs, such as comets and storms, but also personal events, blessings, and curses, like improbably long life, sudden death, or deliverance. As examples:

When Anne Greene was hanged in the 17th Century for a child killing – she did nothing wrong but deliver a deformed stillborn – but she revived in the mortuary later. This was seen as a "clear" sign from heaven that Anne was, indeed, innocent. This was believed so strongly that the Court set her free and saw her absolved of any wrongdoing. The case was widely published and talked about, especially after her former master died only one month later. This was seen as yet another sign compounding the first.

A "sea monster" – probably a whale – washed up on the shores of England in 1588 and was interpreted to presage the coming of the Spanish armada.

In 1643 a parliamentarian account of a battle in Devon remarked that a horrible storm accompanied the forces of the King, a storm so dreadful and extraordinary that "... *lightning and thunder fell upon them, which lightning singed and burned the hair of their heads, and fired the gunpowder in their musket pans...*" People interpreted this as a clear sign of disfavor against the royal forces.

Yet, as perhaps is to be expected, signs were used politically. Shortly after said parliamentarian account, a royal account countered and knew to tell that during the Queen's sea passage a storm had miraculously cleared up, which was read to mean that the blessings from heaven are upon the King and Queen.

Church and biblical tales were accepted at face value, even if there was a lot of strife over interpretation. The assumption that angels and demons existed was an accepted reality. In fact, the people in Tudor and Stuart England believed in a whole host of invisible forces influencing mankind. It stands to reason that, contrary to how BtS works in our day and age, where people will try to explain supernatural events away, Elizabethans and Jacobeans will, in fact, often believe supernatural agencies or divine intervention are at work even when they (perhaps) are not. This is a risk but also an opportunity for monsters. Some canny monster may even set itself up as an angel – just imagine how much more credible the diabolical Syphon Entity would be if its victim/host believes he is acting on a divine command whispered to him by an "angel." It is also an interesting situation for the heroes as they may become famous "magicians" or "soothsayers," or be seen as new Galahads.

People will talk about what they observed and are quick to call in the authorities of church and state, like church wardens, justices of the peace, etc. The psionically gifted or arcanist may soon be hailed as a great magician or an agent of devilry. Tales may travel like wildfire, so be warned. Who knows, Doctor Faustus may have either been the victim of a monster, a misunderstood psychic O.C.C. hero, or a true arcanist, but he certainly got famous for his alleged pact with evil.

Catholic Church ritual was held in Latin, which most people did not understand and which increased the mythical part of the rite. The age of enlightenment did not start before the second half of the 17th Century and did not get into full swing until much, much later. No wonder they were superstitious. Peculiarly, in a BtS game we will prove them right ever and anon.

In order to reflect that people tend to believe in "magic," be that arcane magic or the use of psionics, I suggest changing the rule on the *x1 level* of "Proximity to the Supernatural" (BTS-II, page 31) for Flashing Blades of Horror:

x1 – Under the Microscope (Flashing Blades of Horror version)

When a psychic (or Arcanist) is being observed by fellow mortals, i.e. if there are "mundane" witnesses, he can function completely normally and use his powers! Only when under pressure from the authorities – e.g., certainly when under torture, but also when subjected to less physical stress by being questioned by agents of the Star Chamber, interrogated by the London City Watch, questioned by a Church Warden, or when being a witness or, worse, the accused at court – or subjected to any kind of particular or even scientific scrutiny or laboratory conditions, such as in captivity – the stress of being placed *under the microscope* will have the following consequences:

(1) Spiritual Impotence: 50% chance that the psychic (or Arcanist) becomes spiritually impotent for the duration of the "microscopic attention" plus 1D6x10 minutes. During this period, the psychic (or Arcanist) will stay at base power level, i.e. his power (I.S.P./P.P.E.) cannot be boosted by the proximity to the supernatural.

(2) Reduced Effectiveness: 50% chance that his psionic powers/spells will only work at 50% (halve all power/spell stats like duration, range, damage, etc.).

Weapons and Armor of the Era

Melee Weapons

Use the weapon data from Dead Reign (**Dead Reign® RPG**, pages 114-116) or Palladium Fantasy (**PFRPG core book**, pages 268-269), but here are some important ones:

Rapier: Damage: 1D8

Main Gauche (parrying dagger): Damage: 1D6 (+1 to parry, -1 to strike)

Pike: Damage: 2D6

Halberd: Damage: 3D6

A Note on Black Powder Firearms

In the 15th to 16th Century, firearms are, as a rule, smoothbore muzzle-loaders. Weapon technology in the period mainly evolved around the firing mechanism. Depending on the period, you will find matchlocks (early 16th Century onwards), wheellocks (late 16th Century), and flintlocks (late 16th Century), and some forms in between, like the snaphance, which we will ignore here for the sake of simplicity. At no time in the era covered here did one type of gun completely supplant the other types.

A handgonne is fired by lighting a fuse with an external fire source, like a piece of coal. A matchlock is usually fired by lighting the gunpowder with a pre-lit, slow-burning wick (the match); it is like a slow-burning cannon fuse or a candle wick on the gun. A wheellock was the first self-igniting firearm mechanism with a friction-wheel to cause a spark for firing. A flintlock uses a flint to strike against steel to spark, much like a modern-day cigarette lighter. Wheellock and flintlock are much the same in principle and effect, although it is even said that the wheellock may have been quicker to fire, but the wheel mechanism was much more complex and time-consuming to make, so the less involved and hence cheaper flintlock won over time. For the purposes of the game we will treat wheellock and flintlock as the same thing (rate of fire and misfire rate, see below), and they will only be different in price and availability (wheellock was available earlier and wider than the flintlock, which took over only very late in the 17th Century).

In short, you will find all three types present and available in the 16th and 17th Centuries. The earlier the game is set, the rarer and much more expensive a flintlock will be, and the later the year of your setting, the "cheaper" a matchlock can be had. At all times you might even still find the more primitive 15th Century handgonne in occasional use.

Note, firearms are never inexpensive and there is no gun shack where one can buy them off the shelf. Guns are artfully handcrafted to order! Having a firearm is a badge of rank. There is a reason Sir Walter Raleigh and Robert Dudley had themselves portrayed with their pistols: they were proud of them. A gun could, and often would, cost more than the usual worker's annual salary.

When the word "reliable" is used in connection to all of these firearms, please note the term is <u>very</u> relative. From today's perspective, all these weapons are comparably unreliable, prone to mishaps from simply not working – e.g., because the gunpowder got wet – to horrible misfires.

Actual rifles, i.e. long-barreled, hand-held firearms with grooves put in the barrel of the weapon causing a projectile to spin on the same axis as the line of flight and thus producing more accurate shots, were not in military use before 1750, and even then, anything but widely. Even in the later Napoleonic Wars, rifles were still not seen as the weapon to go to, smoothbore muskets being the rule. Still, you may find the very rare and extremely expensive hand-crafted hunting rifle as far back as the early 16th Century.

Black Powder Firearms Construction Kit!

It is safe to say that, but for the early 16th Century, almost all types of firearms mentioned above could be bought somewhere in all conceivable shapes and sizes. Instead of making an endless list of what are, in the end, very similar weapons, you will find a **firearm construction kit** in the following.

Choose one option in each category (players check with their G.M.s for availability and price):

<u>Lock mechanism</u>: The lock mechanism progressed from handgonne via matchlock and wheellock to flintlock to reduce the rate of misfires and accidents as well as to increase the rate of fire. For the time/actions required to load and for shooting, *see W.P. Black Powder Weapons, below*. The biggest advantage of both the flintlock and the wheellock is that such guns can be carried primed and ready to shoot as they do not require an external ignition of the charge. <u>Misfire rate</u>: Handgonne (20%, i.e. a roll of 1-4 on the D20 for Strike), matchlock (15%, i.e. a roll of 1-3 on the D20 for Strike), wheellock/flintlock (10%, i.e. a roll of 1-2 on the D20 for Strike).

<u>Length of the barrel and thus size of the firearm:</u> Length will determine range. A pistol is only good on a relatively short range (about 50 yards), a carbine is a tad better (about 70 yards), and a long gun like a musket has the best range (about 100 yards). When you buy a firearm, its quality will improve or decrease its range and change it between 50-150%.

<u>Shape of the barrel end:</u> Most firearms have a straight barrel as this gives the best range, but sometimes that is not what you want. A Blunderbuss has a trumpet-like funnel at its end. This spreads the shot loaded to a small area where the shot hits, so that the target is often not only hit by one bullet but by several. However, this barrel type decreases the range quite drastically: half the range for the basic shape, i.e. long gun or pistol.

Rifling: Adding rifling to the barrel will increase the range substantially and make your shots more accurate (+1 strike or more, depending on quality), but will make the firearm extremely expensive and increase loading time, thereby decreasing the rate of fire. If you have the necessary funds, even rifled pistoles were available as early as the late 16th Century. A rifled firearm will have approximately five times (long gun) or twice (pistol and carbine) the range of a smoothbore of the same size.

Caliber: The ammunition was usually a round lead ball, but sometimes simple rectangular cut lead was used instead. Round balls used to have a caliber of 0.3-0.6 for pistols and 0.5-0.8 for long guns. Cut lead is not as easily measured but falls, roughly, in the same categories; after all, the maximum caliber is determined by barrel size. Caliber for a good part determines damage; **assume 1D6 damage per 0.1 of caliber.** Cut lead is easy and cheap to make, and a stripe/length of lead rolled up into a spiral will be carried by many soldiers as spare ammunition; range is reduced by 10%. Damage is equally horrible; cut lead tends to cause worse internal damage while a round ball has better penetration but both are not jacketed and so will expand on and then fragment after impact, causing strong tissue damage. A musket shot may not hit you at 150 yards, but when it hits it will hit like a shotgun slug, ramming into and through their target by sheer weight, shattering bones and smashing organs; exit wounds, if the shot gets so far, which it usually will not contrary to more modern weapons, can be the size of a pomegranate or worse.

Blunderbuss damage: A blunderbuss is usually loaded with a number of lead balls smaller than the caliber of the gun would allow. For purposes of damage, half the damage resulting from the caliber; and 1-3 of the balls will hit a target that has been struck successfully (roll D3). Note, a blunderbuss can also be loaded with iron shards, nails, wood, or even rocks ("shard-shot"). Shard-shot gives a damage bonus of +2.

Examples:

Matchlock Musket: Misfire 15% (1-3 on D20), range 100 yards, straight barrel, no rifling, caliber 0.7 (damage 7D6).

Flintlock Pistol: Misfire 10% (1-2 on D20), range 50 yards, straight barrel, no rifling, caliber 0.5 (damage 5D6).

Wheellock Blunderbuss Pistol (so-called dragon): Misfire 10% (1-2 on D20), range 25 yards, straight barrel with funnel at its end, no rifling. This pistol has a caliber of 0.6, i.e. will do 3D6 damage (+2 for shard-shot) with D3 hits to one target per shot on one strike roll, so up to 9D6 damage on one strike.

How Does Misfire Work?

The following rule is leaning on a similar rule in *Transdimensional TMNT®* (page 68), but rephrased as the supplement is no longer available and to offer an improvement or, at least, an alternative. Most notably, while the original rule introduced an extra percentile misfire roll, I have modified this so that your Strike roll already "contains" the misfire roll. This makes things quicker!

A gun, as a rule, only hits its target on an 8 or higher (BTS-II, page 167), counting bonuses. **If your Strike roll is a natural roll within the misfire range of your gun, you have to roll for the misfire result on the Misfire Table (*below*).** Should you have no Weapon Proficiency, or your weapon is wet or its mechanism damaged, the misfire range may even go beyond 8! As in every case of a roll within the misfire range, bonuses do not count. Your strike generally fails and you must roll on the Misfire Table to see what happens instead.

Unlike modern weapons, black powder weapons were *far* less reliable and prone to mishaps ranging from simple mishaps to an outright weapon explosion. The misfire chance depends on the mechanism of the gun. The mechanism is always some form of primer, and dry powder is essential for a good working of the gun. Misfire chances are increased by the powder getting wet or the mechanism being compromised (*the following are not cumulative*):

Increase the misfire range by 1 for high humidity, e.g. in a swamp area like the Cambridge Fens or the Marais Poitevin north of La Rochelle, unless the gun is kept dry by special care and attention.

Increase the misfire range by 2 when in any sort of rain, unless the gun is kept dry by special care and attention.

Increase the misfire range by 3 when the gun is drenched, e.g. by falling into the water.

Any increase of the misfire chance for wetness disappears when the gun will have properly dried and any wet powder is exchanged for dry powder.

The misfire chance will also increase when the weapon has taken damage to the lock mechanism:

Increase the misfire range by 1D6 when the firing mechanism of the gun has been damaged but not destroyed. Every instance of parrying with a black powder weapon carries a 15% risk of such damage. Likewise, a black powder weapon falling from a height may get damaged for a similar add-on to the misfire rate. Whatever the cause, such increase of the misfire range will go away upon proper repair of the weapon by a gunsmith.

Increase the misfire range by 1 (for blunderbusses) when shard-shot damages the barrel. Any type of shard-shot used stands a chance of 20% per shot (!) to damage the barrel and increase the misfire rate of the blunderbuss by 1 for every time the barrel is damaged by a shard-shot until repaired by a gunsmith.

Increase the misfire range by 2 when a gun has been damaged by overload.

Misfire Table

01-25% Misfire. The weapon should have fired, but it did not. Maybe the match was not properly ignited, or the powder a little too wet. Matchlocks need to be cleaned and the match re-lit (cost: 2 actions for cleaning/re-lighting, plus 1 action for the new shot); all other guns just need the hammer cocked again and the gun can be shot again as soon as in the next action (cost: 1 action for the new shot).

26-40% Bad Load. The weapon must be cleaned out and reloaded, which will take 1D4 melee rounds, including the round of the misfire if the shooter has actions left.

41-55% Jammed. The firing mechanism is damaged somehow and the weapon must be disassembled and put back together, which will take 2D6 melee rounds, including the round of the misfire if the shooter has actions left. There is a 25% chance that the gun requires the attention of a gunsmith to work again, which the character will know only either with a successful Gunsmith check or after reassembling.

56-70% Fizzle. The gun goes off very noisily with a small fireworks display of bright sparkles, but the shot just rolls slowly out of the barrel. No damage is sustained by either the gun or anyone else. Reload and try again.

71-80% Hangfire or Slow Burn. Like a firecracker that apparently fizzles out, only to go off with a slight delay. Will discharge in 1D6 actions (G.M. should roll this!), which may lead to unfortunate accidents if the gun is, for example, being cleaned or checked on to determine why it misfired when the shot discharges. The character may alternatively opt to continue to aim and wait for the shot, wasting further actions on the shot, then roll a normal strike if he waited long enough – he may get the benefit of aiming, though.

81-90% Overloaded. Either the powder used was too strong or too much powder was used. Target will take double damage if hit! However, the weapon is destroyed and the shooter takes 2D6 damage himself.

91-00% Explosion. The shot does not go to the target, but the weapon blows up and is destroyed. The shooter takes 4D6 damage (2D6 if the weapon itself is not capable of inflicting 4D6 damage with a single shot).

Intentional Overload

Any black powder weapon can be overloaded intentionally, either by using stronger powder or just more. This is very hard to control, and any overloading risks the destruction of the gun. You need to have W.P. Black Powder Weapons to try it at all and have a chance of not destroying your weapon. For any attempt at intentionally overloading, the gun will be destroyed 60% of the time. If you make the destruction roll successfully, i.e. not destroying the gun, you will still have damaged your weapon and have a +2 misfire rate in the future until a, probably costly, repair. The overloaded gun will do double damage to the target; plus 2D6 to the shooter in case of a "destroyed" result. There is no way to "learn" to do this better.

Using Black Powder Weapons Without the W.P.

As with all "modern weapons," anyone can use a gun. The rules for "No Weapon Proficiency" in the BtS-II rule book (page 215) apply and the unskilled user is at a severe disadvantage, i.e. he does not receive any bonuses, cannot make a Called or Aimed Shot, does not even know how to load and maintain the gun, etc. However, as Black Powder Weapons are more difficult to handle than more modern weapons, the

basic (not the modified) *misfire chance doubles for any unskilled use.*

Explosives

Black Powder is also a wonderful explosive weapon when used as a grenade and, if packed properly, can bring down walls. The following two weapon entries are leaning heavily on *The Magic of Science in Palladium Fantasy,* by Greg Diaczyk, **The Rifter® #10**, page 19.

Grenade: A small pouch with some shrapnel like rocks or nails and about 4 ounces (113 grams) of black powder will do 4D6 damage to a 5 foot (1.5 m) area. If stuffed properly between a door and its frame, e.g. near the lock, it will do 1D6x10 damage to the door in addition to the abovementioned 4D6 to anyone standing within 5 feet (1.5 m) to catch the spray.

Bomb: A small sack or satchel filled with similar material and about 10 ounces (283 grams) of black powder will do 2D6x10 to a 10 foot (3 m) area. If packed properly in or under a wall at a weak point, it will do 1D4x100 to the structure and the aforementioned 2D6x10 to anyone in the blast radius of 10 feet (3 m).

Body Armor

Use the Armor data from Dead Reign (**Dead Reign® RPG**, page 117) or Palladium Fantasy (**PFRPG**, page 270). The latter also has nifty rules for horse barding and armor repair times.

Swashbuckling!

Among the core elements of a swashbuckling adventure are sword fights and swashbuckling antics. I have therefore suggested some new weapons (see above) and will now go into swashbuckling, which is more than "just" fencing. The article "Flashing Blades" in **The Rifter® #22** gives very good rules for fencing, but it is very much geared on dueling; you can, of course, use that in lieu of or in addition to some of the following Swashbuckling antics and stunts. I have gone to some length to use the rules as they are in Megaversal canon, sometimes borrowing from other game lines as and how I saw fit. As with all rules treatments and interpretations, please feel free to use or discard, adapt or adopt.

In any case, your swashbuckling experience will be greater when you do not run a combat merely by an exchange of straight D20 rolls on strike-parry-strike-dodge, and so on, but let your actions be augmented by wit and special moves. The bread and butter of any swashbuckling movie or book are the many stunts the fighters pull during a melee. I am sure there are many more, but in the following I want to give some examples and how I suggest to handle them under the rules to let you, literally, pull your own stunts.

Blade Lock: A blade lock works as described for *Entangle* on pages 159 & 162 of BtS-II. The fighter uses his blade (or when using W.P. Paired Weapons with two blades, one of his blades) to lock his blade with the blade of his opponent. If he

36

successfully entangles the blade thusly, this is a great opportunity to, for example, use *Blade Pushback* (costs 1 attack), say something witty (no action cost), close in and headbutt (costs 1 attack), or if he uses W.P. Paired Weapons, use his second blade to strike home. Note, in the latter case, if the opponent is only fighting with one weapon, he will be *unable* to parry with a locked blade, so that he can only dodge. If he dodges successfully, he will either weave to the side or jump back. In either case, the blade lock would be broken en passant with defending successfully against the attack.

Blade Pushback: The fighter uses his blade to push his opponent forcefully back. This is resolved by a normal strike roll with all applicable bonuses. The combatant either holds his weapon with two hands to do so, which is even possible with a sword without damaging yourself as long as you are wearing gauntlets, or uses the lower end of the blade (shoulder) to push, preferably when the blades are already locked (see *Blade Lock*) as the opponent then could not parry the pushback. Unless the blades are already locked when *Blade Pushback* is used, the opponent can deflect the pushback with dodge or parry. If *Blade Pushback* is successful, however, the opponent will be pushed back 1D4/2 yards and perhaps even knocked down (roll percentile; the percentage chance of knockdown is the pusher's P.S. +20, minus the opponent's P.S.).

Blinding Attack: This can be done a number of ways, like shining a lantern beam, throwing sand or powder of some sort into your opponent's eyes. A *Blinding Attack* takes 1 action. You suffer a -8 Strike penalty on this variant *Called Shot*. If the attack is not dodged or parried (when at all possible), the foe must make a *Save vs Pain* or be blinded for 1D10 actions (and -5 to *Strike*, *Parry* and *Dodge*). Especially hurtful matter, for example, pepper powder, harsh schnaps, or lemon juice, will increase the period as it "burns" longer in the eyes (plus 1D10 actions or worse on G.M. discretion). Important: A *Blinding Attack* made with a lantern in a dark environment will likewise leave the victim blinded for an additional 1D10 actions, as his eyes will need longer to adjust. A variant *Blinding Attack* is made by covering the opponent's head with a cloak, but that is handled as an *Entangle* (see W.P. Cloak Fighting) instead.

Door Slam: The opportunity may arise when you stand near a door and an opponent rushes you. Strike by forcefully opening the door into the opponent's body. Essentially this is an improvised slam attack which you can do if the door opens the right way. Damage is 1D6, but you do not get any damage or W.P. strike bonuses. The opponent cannot parry the door but dodge and, if hit, roll with the impact for half damage. However, on an unsuccessful dodge the defender will loose his footing and fall down, losing initiative and 1 attack.

Feint: A feint is a combat bluff. It is the technique to lead your opponent along. The feinting fighter pretends to either do something – like moving his body and arm "just so" to suggest that his next action will be a certain strike, or make himself open to a certain strike – while in fact planning to execute something else. A feint is used to goad an opponent to do something that the feinting fighter has prepared for – he sets a trap. If it works you will have an advantage that will do you a lot of good against any opponent and may even level the playing field on your next strike. If it fails, though, you will have spent 2 actions for nothing but a weak strike.

Feint uses up 2 actions – 1 for the feint and 1 for the following strike. If combined with e.g. a power punch the total cost will be 3 actions. The actions are spent no matter whether the feint is successful or not. The feinter just has to declare that he will feint before rolling a strike. The opponent gets a *Perception* check to determine if he is going to detect the feint and rolls against a difficulty level of 8 (moderate challenge) if the feinting fighter has a lower level in his weapon proficiency and against 14 (challenging) if the feinting fighter has a better weapon proficiency level. The difficulty level is then increased by the parry bonus of the feinting fighter and decreased by the parry and Perception bonus of the opponent. If the feint is successful, the deceived fighter does not receive any bonuses on his parry or dodge against the incoming strike! However, if the feint is detected, the undeceived opponent clearly sees the plan of the failed feinter, who consequently loses all bonuses for the following strike roll.

Example: Chevalier du Bois attacks the Marquis Le Clé with a feint. The good Marquis has a Perception bonus of +2 and a parry bonus of +2 and his W.P. Rapier is at 6th level, while the Chevalier has a parry bonus of +3 but is not as experienced with his rapier – his W.P. Rapier is only at 3rd level. Du Bois cleverly pretends to make a high strike, opening his left side to the Marquis' strike, and that way wishes to goad him to move to exploit the "mistake." However, du Bois sneakily plans to quickly make a slashing cut instead. Le Clé now has to roll against a 7 (8+3-2-2) – "moderate challenge" as the feinting fighter is not as good as the defender, +3 feinting fighter's parry bonus, -2 defender's perception bonus, -2 defender's parry bonus – and comes up with a 13! Bad luck for du Bois, the Marquis saw through the feint. Thus, Du Bois now strikes without bonuses. Marquis Le Clé parries with disdainful ease. This would be an ideal situation for the Marquis to use *Witty Repartee* to taunt the Chevalier to lose his cool.

Hanging from or swinging on a rope fighting: Fighting in such a difficult and challenging position takes away all your bonuses from strike, parry and dodge as you will have to concentrate on the rope movement more than anything else. However, if you have the *Gymnastics* or *Acrobatics* skills you will fight at all your bonuses (P.P., W.P.) only halved instead. Also, unless your enemy is trying to get to YOU or you simply hang on, it is not easy to maneuver to get to the right place. To maneuver, i.e. swing in the right direction at the right moment, roll a P.P. check using the Perception Roll difficulties (BtS-II, page 170) and adding only your P.P. bonus to the roll; normally, a challenge rating of 10 or 12 will be appropriate. You will succeed if you hit the challenge rating number. Normally, this movement does not cost an action (any strike, parry, etc. you do while swinging/hanging on the rope will, of course, still cost you the appropriate number of actions), but if you fail, your swing is off and you will have lost one action. If you have *Sense of Balance*, as provided by the *Gymnastics* and *Acrobatics* skills, you can use this skill instead of the P.P. check.

Hazardous Jumping (jumping on a running horse or from a horse to a coach, etc.): Roll a P.P. check using the

Perception Roll difficulties (BtS-II, page 170) and adding only your P.P. bonus to the roll; normally, a challenge rating of 10 or 12 will be appropriate. If you have *Back Flip*, as provided by the *Gymnastics* and *Acrobatics* skills, you can use this skill instead of the P.P. check. You will succeed if your roll meets or exceeds the challenge rating. If you fail, you will take damage from falling (*Roll with Impact* for half damage) and, potentially, may be trampled by a horse or rolled over by the coach, etc. In case such latter further negative consequence looms, roll a dodge to avoid it.

Headbutt: A headbutt is a risky move, but may sometimes be the best option in close quarters. This attack strikes opponent with the blunt part of the head, preferably the crown. Roll to strike normally, and damage is 1D6 plus bonuses. Knockout on a Natural 20. If an opponent defends any headbutt attack with a Natural 20, the attacker is knocked out instead.

Masking your action (like flourishing your hat elaborately to hide drawing a throwing knife with the other hand): Masking your action essentially makes your strike more elaborate, it adds a sneaky flourish; a masked strike costs two actions. Depending on what you hide and how, one of the following skills will help. You can either use *Palming* for some deft sleight of hand with smaller objects or *Concealment* if you tucked it away in your clothing. The opponent trying to unmask your sneaky action, may roll one of these skills as well – it takes a thief to catch a thief, eh? – and will succeed if his skill check succeeds by a greater margin than your Palming/Concealment attempt. Or, the defender may roll Perception. A successful Palming/Concealment sets the Perception attempt at a challenge rating of 14. If you do not have the Palming/Concealment skills you can still mask your action by simply declaring how. The opponent's chance to perceive your masking attempt then only has a difficulty of 8, though. If the masking attempt was undetected, the opponent can still parry or dodge but does not receive any bonuses to his defense.

Parrying with an Unusual Implement (fork, candle holder, furniture, etc.): The canny fighter can use everything around him to fight. See *Using Improvised Weapons* below. As a rule, you get no combat bonuses to strike or parry at all. Unusual implements are not suited for parrying. They are not balanced and typically do not sit well in your hand, so your grip on them is not as good as on a tool made for fighting. Many of them, such as stools, are not made to sustain a strike from a weapon. To see if you lose your grip or the unusual implement gets destroyed on a successful parry, let the attacker roll damage against the unusual implement. If the damage exceeds more than *three times* the maximum base damage capacity (a bottle has a base damage of 1D4, its maximum base damage capacity is thus 4; cf. below under *Using Improvised Weapons*), your *Unusual Implement* will be destroyed or beaten out of your hand (G.M. decision).

Pommeling the Opponent: Strike the enemy with the pommel or guard of the sword. It is what you may opt for if you either do not have enough room, want to catch your opponent off guard, or daze instead of kill. Damage is 1D4 plus any bonuses. While this is a blunt attack, W.P. Sword covers this use of the sword as well and any strike bonuses you may have for sword uses will apply.

Pulling a rug out from under your opponent: This stunt takes 1 action. Roll a strike roll plus (only) bonuses from P.P., defender gets a dodge roll to jump away in time or may just elect to "stand his ground." Pulling out a rug from under your opponent only works if your lifting weight capacity (BtS-II, page 135) is greater than the weight of the opponent standing on the rug. If more than one person or object is on the rug, add the weights to see if you are strong enough to pull the rug out. Anyone having the rug pulled out from under him will fall to the ground, lose initiative and one action immediately, and will be prone until he gets up again.

Table Slam: Use a nearby table and push it into an opponent rushing you. This is not throwing a table; that is handled under Using Improvised Weapons. With Table Slam you are using a table to slide it forcefully along the floor where it stands into the way of an opponent. Range is 1 foot (0.3 m) per point of P.S., but may be modified according to the conditions of the floor (G.M. discretion). You can use the table for this attack only if its weight is lower than your lifting weight capability (BtS-II, page 135). Damage is 1D6, but you do not get any damage or W.P. strike bonuses. The opponent cannot parry the table but can dodge and, if hit, roll with the impact for half damage. However, on an unsuccessful dodge, the defender will lose his footing and fall down, losing initiative and 1 attack.

Off-Hand Fencing: Remember that scene in "The Princess Bride" when Inigo Montoya and The Dread Pirate Roberts fight on the top of the Cliffs of Despair? They surprise each other by each switching their rapier from hand to hand. Having a W.P. in a handheld weapon usually will mean that you have been trained to fence with both hands, if not equally well, then at least with some ease, but when you fight, you get used to your opponent's stance and right of left leaning moves. A switch of fighting hand in the middle of a melee will probably leave you surprised for a moment until you can recover, but this is a costly ruse. The fighter intending such a surprise must first spend at least 3 rounds fighting with his "off" hand at a -1 to strike before switching to his "better" hand. When he does so, he will gain initiative automatically and the surprised opponent will be at -3 to parry for the full "surprise" round, unless he can counter with a like "off-handed" move.

Rappelling down curtains or sails by tearing the fabric with a dagger: Use the Rappelling sub-skill of *Climbing* or the *Gymnastics* Climb Rope/Rappel skill. If you have *Acrobatics* use your Climb Rope skill halved. If you have none of these skills, you will be in for a high risk ride with a percentage chance to pull off this stunt equal to your P.P. stat (e.g., P.P. of 10 will give you a 10% chance). If you should not succeed, you will fall.

Ship to ship combat (Boarding and Naval Action): I recommend to look at and use or adapt the rules from *Palladium Fantasy Book 3: Adventures on the High Seas*, page 190. Incidentally, you will also find some interesting naval skills in the same book (pages 7-9), which you can adapt. The ship types alone – pages 178-181 of said book – make it worth a look as those ships can be used as they are for the Elizabethan and Tudor age, including galleys, which were used in the Mediterranean until the 18th Century.

Without Sea Legs Modifier: That said, for a quick and simple rule for hand to hand combat and other fighting actions on board a ship: ships are unsteady surfaces – anyone fighting without having acquired his *"sea legs"* first will be at -3 to strike/parry/dodge and -25% to any skill use that requires being sure of foot and hand, such as Climbing, etc. Characters with a naval background, or after some time and training aboard a ship (G.M. discretion), will reduce this negative modifier over time up to a point when they fight unimpaired, and they may even start at "0" if particularly well-trained (like the Freebooter occupation), except for circumstantial modifiers. Circumstantial modifiers, as from a sudden hard wave rocking the ship or fighting in a torrential downpour, always go on top of any other modifiers, including the "without sea legs" -3/-25%.

Swinging on chandeliers: Works like *Hanging from or swinging on a rope fighting*, see above.

Tightrope fighting (fencing on thin rooftops or on other precarious footing, like on a ship's rigging): Anyone finding himself in a position to fight on precarious footing such as this will strike/dodge/parry at -5, unless he rolls a successful *Walk Tightrope* or *Sense of Balance* at the beginning of his round. The latter roll has to be made every round, once a round. If it is successful, you will not suffer the -5, but not get any P.P. bonuses and fight only with your W.P. bonuses to strike/parry/dodge. A *Blade Pushback* can be lethal under these circumstances. Any hefty movement – such as body flip, dodge, tackle, power punch, roll with impact – or movement leaving the precarious footing – such as leaps or kick attacks – will necessitate a re-roll of *Walk Tightrope* or *Sense of Balance* or result in a fall. You have to keep your movement economical on precarious footing.

Using Improvised Weapons (melee and thrown): Sometimes you just do not have a weapon at hand, want to surprise your opponent with an unorthodox attack, or are in a brawl and do not want draw your weapon but much rather use the "more harmless" chair/bottle/etc. Any character can pick up about anything and use it as a weapon, be it the bottle (empty or not), chair, table, etc. You basically use it the item as a club, provided they are within your weight carrying capacity. I have deliberately elected the carrying capacity as you have to swing the thing and not only lift it. See also on page 135 (BtS-II) for throwing improvised weapons ("awkward objects ... not designed for throwing"). Once hoisted, you can inflict substantial damage with some of these implements, provided you hit. Improvised Weapons are weapons that are not made for fighting as they are not balanced and for which no training is available; thus, you get no combat bonuses to strike or parry (i.e. no W.P. or P.P. bonuses) when using an improvised weapon – "Using Weapons," BtS-II, page 164.

Heavy book: 1 point of damage (Note: A book can also be used to catch a blade between the pages – this is treated as an *Entangle* action at +1.)

Fork: 1D2

Bottle: 1D4

Candle Holder: 1D4

Broken Bottle: 1D4+1

Stool: 1D6

Heavy chair: 2D6

Door, unhinged: 3D6

Table: 4D6

Heavy or bulky items – like unhinged doors or tables – consume two actions for one normal attack or three for a power punch.

Note: W.P. Blunt does apply to using clubs and club-like implements, like a pipe or a branch, which arguably could be seen to fall into the "improvised" category. This is a G.M. decision. The closer the item misappropriated to serve as a weapon is to a tool designed to be blunt weapon, like a cudgel, the more it should be seen to be covered by W.P. Blunt. The farther away it is to anything close to a balanced weapon, like a chair, the less it should be considered to receive the benefits of W.P. Blunt.

A G.M. may, under special circumstances, allow a player to develop a W.P. dedicated to a certain improvised weapon, such as "W.P. Fork," but only for items that are conceivably conducive to combat training, which most furniture simply is not. Note, the new weapon proficiency *W.P. Trick Fencing* has a trick that allows parrying with unusual implements. In a pinch, I suggest to use the bonuses as given for W.P. Chain (BtS-II, page 213). While such a dedicated weapon proficiency will be a skill slot misspent in most cases as the unusual "weapon" will not lose its disadvantages, like breakability, it may add flair to, for example, an old fencing master type of character.

Skills from the Core Book

The following skills do not apply to a *Flashing Blades of Horror* game:

Communication Skills: Electronic Countermeasures, Laser Communication, Optic Systems, Radio: Basic, TV/Video.

Electrical Skills: All.

Mechanical Skills: Aircraft Mechanic, Automotive Mechanic, Robot Mechanic.

Medical Skills: Crime Scene Investigation, Psychology.

Military Skills: Aircraft: Combat Helicopter, Aircraft: Jet Fighters, APC & Tanks, Demolitions, Demolitions: Underwater, NBC Warfare.

Rogue Skills: Computer Hacking; Science Skills: Artificial Intelligence, Astrophysics, Genetics, Psychology.

Technical Skills: Computer Operation, Computer Programming, Photography.

Transportation Skills: Aircraft: Helicopter, Aircraft: Jet, Airplane, Automobile, Bicycling, Boats: Motor, Race & Hydrofoil Types, Motorcycles & Snowmobiles, Tracked Vehicles, Truck, Water Scooter, Water Skiing & Surfing.

W.P. Modern Weapons: All *except* W.P. Trick Shooting.

All other skills apply. Note, however, that no skill will convey know-how, ability, or education beyond the bounds of what was known, or conceivably known, at the age of the game (G.M. discretion). I have left in some skills that were not academic disciplines in 1500-1700 per se, but do not hurt (for example: Anthropology). You may want to reintroduce some skills, for example: "Aircraft: Combat Helicopters" if in your setting the da Vinci helicopter was actually built and could take off. As always, please make your own more or less rigorous judgment calls.

New Skills

Court Etiquette (*Domestic*)

A clear understanding of the way the court and the households of nobles and the gentry work, including the rules on proper behavior (when to bow, when to retreat, how to introduce yourself, who speaks first, etc.), courtly procedures, official and "private courtly" functions, and routines, what is appropriate to wear to which occasion, where to sit (how far or close to the monarch, etc.), how to deal with the royal (and other authorities) bureaucracy, who to contact to get things done, where to get a land deed stamped, and other useful information in matters of protocol and conduct. **Base Skill:** 30% +3% per level.

Diplomacy (*Technical*)

Diplomacy is the art of making deals or breaking them "the right way," the knowledge of negotiation techniques and tricks, and an acute sense of social environments in a negotiation setting or in political venues, like in parliament or at court. A diplomat can negotiate terms; a side effect of that is that the price of goods can be reduced by negotiation depending on how well you negotiate (amount is G.M. discretion). A diplomat can also, importantly, "feel the room" and, when he has been in a certain political setting long enough, will get a sense about who deals with whom, who is trusted, who is feared, what rumors abound, perhaps even who spreads them and to make an educated guess on why. Feel the room essentially also works as a Detect Social Ambush skill and a character may be able to understand the negative tension against him just timely enough to make good his escape before the social ambush will be sprung. **Base Skill:** Negotiation: 35% +5% per level. Feel the Room/Detect Social Ambush: 25% +3% per level.

Drive Coach / Horse-Cart (*Transportation*)

Skill for driving any cart, wagon or coach drawn by one or more horses, mules, donkeys or oxen, and the in-depth knowledge to (I) assess the quality of such vehicle, its draft animals, and how well they work together as well as (ii) how to harness the animals, and (iii) care for the vehicle and the animals. With this skill, various methods of harnessing are known such as the Middle-Ages way where the animals were arrayed in single file, or the modern way to put two (or more) animals side by side, possibly even a draft team with more than one row. **Base Skill**: Drive Coach: 60% +5% per level. Assess Quality: 70% +5% per level. Care & Harness: 80% +3% per level.

Farming (*Technical*)

Everything you need to be a farmer, i.e. including the knowledge of the land, how to till the soil, which crops grow well under which conditions and on which type of land, which farming implements to use for what purpose, how the weather will influence the yield, etc. **Base Skill**: 35% +5%.

Savoir Vivre (*Domestic*)

Savoir Vivre is to know how to live, or, to be more precise before someone confuses it with bookkeeping, it is the art of living well, move gracefully through society, and enjoying the moment. It does not convey a knowledge of prices, pricing, barter, *Wardrobe & Grooming* or *Cooking*, but it allows appreciation of food, drink, and attire and represents the knowledge about which convenience and luxury is appreciated more in society and for what reasons and where it comes from. A person with *Savoir Vivre* can always distinguish a Bordeaux from a Burgundy wine, a Cuban from a Dominican cigar, and knows which vest color and decoration ("*it is pearls this year, silver trim is so yesterday*") is en vogue. It also allows the skilled to move through better society, hold enchanting small talk, as well as making and appreciating an artful compliment and saying sweet nothings, allowing to flirt with the best of them. The skill has to be taken once for a cluster of societies (Western & Middle Europe; Eastern Europe; Ottoman Empire; etc.). It is the skill you need in a genteel environment and, especially, at the courts of Europe. *Savoir Vivre* is not a fighting skill but a courtier without it is in dire peril as a faux pas, a wrong step, can lead to loss of favor, may be a slight to be erased only in a duel, result in banishment or even death. **Base Skill**: Appreciate Food, Drink, Attire, and Luxury: 40% +4% per level; Know Society Preference: 60% +5% per level; Flirtation: 20% +3% per level + Charm/Impress bonus.

Theology (*Science*)

Knowledge and the scientific study, reasoning and discussion of the divine as well as the understanding of religious traditions, history, criticisms, primary and secondary texts, sources, and relics. Note, this skill is recommended as an additional skill alongside *Lore: Religion*. Lore: Religion covers a wide range of religions and concentrates on the paranormal according to its skill category. *Theology* is the noble scientific pursuit as taught, for example, at Heidelberg, Oxford and Cambridge and the Catholic seminars of France and Rome. **Base Skill**: 30% +5% per level; +10% bonus to Theology if the character also has Philosophy; gives a +5% bonus to Public Speaking when used in a theological context.

Witty Repartee

(*Communication, Rogue*)

A skill no swashbuckler can be without. The age of flashing blades is a time when the impromptu couplet and the witty quip were essential skills. You know what to say to artfully taunt, wax poetically, and brag just right. With a successful check on *Witty Repartee*, however you flaunt yourself, you will be believed or, at least, admired for the moment (as long as the conversation lasts plus a few minutes until a reality check has a chance to set it), or your skillful taunt will really sting. A successful taunt may also just give you that extra moment you need in a fight and you gain initiative while your opponent sputters angrily, unless he can counter by a like successful *Witty Repartee* (one will then cancel out the other) or with a successful save vs "Insanity." **Base Skill**: Taunt: 30% +5% per level; Flaunt: 40% +3% per level.

W.P. Black Powder Incendiaries

(*W.P. Modern Weapons*)

Weapon Proficiency to prepare, manipulate, and use black powder incendiaries.

W.P. Black Powder Weapons

(*W.P. Modern Weapons*)

Only with W.P. Black Power Weapons does one receive bonuses to shooting guns as attribute bonuses from P.P. and Hand to Hand bonuses do not apply to guns. Without the W.P., characters can still shoot without any bonuses, but do not know how to load, clean or maintain the gun, and suffer double the base misfire chance.

W.P. Bonuses: +1 to strike at levels 1, 3, 6, 10, and 14. Character can ultimately fire a black powder weapon faster than those without the W.P.

Rate of Fire: The rate of fire of black powder front-loaders – or, as with some rare examples of handgonnes, breech-loaders – is determined by the loading time. There, wheellock and flintlock guns have an advantage as they can be carried around pre-loaded and fired at a later time. Pre-loading does not gain any time for handgonnes or matchlocks as they are better prepared fresh and, its main delaying factor, they have to be fired by lighting a match (handgonne) or touching a live match to the pan (matchlock). Rate of fire is either loading plus shooting time or, in the case of a pre-load, just shooting time.

Loading Time: With all black powder weapons, preparing the gun for shooting is the really time consuming part. The good news is this activity can be improved, usually by drills. Historically, for a wheel- or flintlock musket, about 2-4 shots a minute were to be expected, 4 shots per minute was actually the drill aim of the English Army in the 18th Century, and up to a maximum of 6 are seen as probably possible. That said, for loading you can use all actions you get from your Hand to Hand style, but not the additional attack from the Boxing skill. Loading time with a matchlock, wheellock or flintlock: 5 actions/attacks at 1st level proficiency, 4 actions/attacks at 3rd level, and 3 actions/attacks at 7th level. Loading time with a handgonne: 4 actions/attacks.

Shooting Time: A shot always takes 1 attack for wheellock or flintlock weapons, but 2 attacks for matchlock guns and handgonnes. For the latter two, actively igniting the charge is part of the shooting. *Targeting* and *Called Shots*, if employed, will add 1 attack each to the total APM cost. Handgonnes are two-handed guns, even small handgonnes, and all need a stand, tripod, or other rest for targeting or Called Shots.

Stress increases loading time and basic misfire rate: Imagine a cavalry charge against you. You stand there and your best option to stop the charge is to shoot the horse or rider. Your only problem: your black powder weapon is not loaded yet. Now, you have a matchlock musket; you will have to go through 28 steps to get the thing ready to fire. As you are well drilled and trained, you know you have to go about this in a calm and collected manner. If you miss a step or go about it wrong, you will at best increase your chances of misfire if it works at all. There is a reason why some soldiers did not shoot their bullet but instead shot the ramrod they had left sticking in their musket, owing to stress or sloppiness while loading. In case you are loading while under stress (G.M. discretion), like being under attack or in another life threatening situation, *loading time is doubled and misfire is +1* unless you make a Horror Factor save vs a target of 12 (or the Horror Factor of whatever is coming, whichever is higher).

Sloppy loading increases the basic misfire rate: You can shorten the loading time by deliberately rushing it. That is entirely the decision of the shooter, but it is a dangerous call. Sloppy load *doubles the base misfire rate* of your gun, but loading time is halved.

A Note on All Guns:

(1) Loading while moving/unbalanced: The character loses all bonuses and doubles the action/attack cost for loading when doing so when running, flying/levitating, riding on horseback or on a rapidly moving vehicle like a quick coach, or while otherwise unbalanced.

(2) Firing a gun while doing something else at the same time, e.g. parrying, is possible, but will make the shoot a wild shot at -6 to strike, and Called Shots or aiming are impossible.

(3) Bursts and sprays are impossible with black powder weapons.

(4) Firing at moving targets is -3 to strike, but -6 to strike anything moving faster than 50 mph (80 km), which will be extremely rare in the 17th and 16th Centuries, or, albeit slower, partially covered, like a rider on a horse or a coachman. All modifiers are cumulative.

W.P. Cannon

(*W.P. Modern Weapons*)

Familiarity with heavy artillery, including sea and land-based artillery, and basically any black powder weapon heavier than a "handheld" gun. This skill covers, in particular, weapons like the falconet, falcon, saker, culverin, bombards, and cannons of all types. Most cannons are front-loaders, only a very few are breech-loaders, and all cannons are smoothbore. The truly heavy artillery, i.e. beyond 20 pounds (9 kg), will usually not be found on ships – again, depending on the exact time – but are pretty "immovable" siege weapons. A normal army will not carry cannons above 12-pounders. The number of men, horses and wagons you need to transport, assemble, and use the very heavy artillery is not suited to any form of quick army movement.

Damage: The damage depends mainly upon the weight of the shot, as well as on the type. The following covers only full ball shot. A 1-pounder will do 8D6 damage, a 3-pounder will do 1D4x10, a 6-pounder 1D6x10, a 12-pounder 1D10x10, a 20-pounder 2D10x10, a 32-pounder 3D10x10, a 50-pounder 1D4x100, an 80-pounder 1D6x100, a 100-pounder 1D10x100, and a 120-pounder 2D10x100. One to three times the weight of the ball in black powder will be required to propel the shot forth.

Average Range: 1 pound falconet 5,000 feet (1,524 m), a 6 pound saker 7,400 feet (2.3 km), a 32 pound demi-cannon 1,600 feet (488 m), etc. For larger cannons, the heavier the shot, the smaller the range.

Misfire: Use the misfire rules as outlined above for black powder weapons; misfire chance is 20%, i.e. a roll of 1-4 on the D20 for strike. The effects can be truly devastating and, in case of any explosive result, the damage dealt will be commensurate to the damage capacity of the cannon itself! A cannon can help sink its own ship or "merely" send its crew flying.

Typical Payload: 1 shot.

Special: Bombarding infantry or cavalry for a few shots requires them to make a Horror Factor check, modified by the leadership they are under, or they will break rank and flee.

W.P. Bonuses: +1 to strike at levels 1, 3, 6, 10, and 14.

W.P. Cloak Fighting

(*Weapon Proficiencies*)

A very special fencing skill, but there really was a school teaching it. It may seem a little peculiar at first until you have seen it in action. A cloak was a fashionable piece of clothing in the time period covered here, so it was often available. In an age with so much fighting, it made sense to build making use of the cloak into the art of fencing. A cloak offers no damage capability per se but for the modes of employment described. Can be used one-handed. Cloak Fighting may be used with W.P. Paired Weapon, so that the user can use the cloak to parry/entangle/blind/snare and attack (or parry) with e.g. the rapier in his other hand at the same time and in the same action.

W.P. Bonuses: +1 to strike to entangle, snare, or blind at levels 2, 5, 8, 11, and 15. +1 to parry at levels 1, 3, 5, 8, and 11.

Active Parry: There is no automatic parry with a cloak. Parrying costs 1 action (see above with respect to W.P. Paired Weapons). In this way the cloak is not used coiled around the arm to absorb damage – a cloak, even a thick one, is after all,

only made of cloth and thus offers little in the way of additional protection – but is swung and swirled around snappily, to brush a weapon to the side, or confusingly, to make the defender and his movements harder to see or guess.

Entangle: Entangling is a special defensive move with a cloak and works as described for *Entangle* on pages 159 & 162 of BtS-II. The cloak user entangles either the weapon or the arm of his opponent. Entangle is a defensive action used instead of parrying or dodging, but can be kept up for several rounds, unless the opponent breaks free (BtS-II, page 162).

Blind & Entangle: An Entangle attack on the head for a -8 to strike. If successful the cloak is slung around the opponent's head and blinds him, as per the rule on page 161 of BtS-II. The opponent suffers the disadvantages as described for *Blind*.

Snare Opponent's Weapon: The weapon becomes entangled and is pulled out of opponent's hand. A natural, unmodified (no bonus) roll of 18, 19, or 20 will disarm an opponent in this way, unless he can roll an equally, unmodified high parry (no bonuses).

W.P. Fencing

(BtS-II, page 207)

W.P. Paired Weapons

(BtS-II, page 214)

W.P. Quick Draw

(BtS-II, page 214)

W.P. Trick Fencing

Can choose 1 trick at 1st level of W.P., a 2nd trick at 4th, 3rd trick at 7th, 4th trick at 10th, and the 5th trick at 14th.

1. Can fence while hanging upside down or while hanging onto or swinging on something (rope, chandelier, etc.); all bonuses to strike and from W.P. Sword and W.P. Fencing are fully applicable.

2. Can throw his fencing sword quite accurately, but strike bonuses are half and a "Called Shot" is impossible.

3. Dodge, roll or somersault and come up fighting (normally coming up like this would result in a "wild shot" penalty to strike at -6 and consume 1 extra action, but not so with this trick!), no bonuses or penalties to strike; straight roll of the dice.

4. Parrying with an improvised implement not made for parrying, like a chair, fork, plate, etc. at full P.P. parrying bonus (normally half) and automatic parry.

5. Leave a mark. Instead of striking for damage, this strike, if successful, does only 1 point of damage but leaves a mark like the famous "Z." Only simple signs can be struck this way.

Social Status

You can create characters according to the core rules. However, a few elements would be lacking. The following tables are geared towards role-playing and adventure set in the Elizabethan and Stuart age. You will, for example, according to the tables, not be able to start the game as a Lieutenant, the Commander of the Musketeers, or the Prince of Wales (Dauphin in France), but your family may be highly (or lowly) placed. There is a good bit of adventure in that. If you like a party of princes, go ahead, but it is not as colorful and conducive to adventuring as, say, starting out as the bastard son of a duke, or a criminal having grown up in the catacombs of Vienna, or the son of a poor country squire with scant connections in the capital. As always, provided your G.M. allows it, feel free to modify or ignore results or instead of rolling it up, cherry pick. Family heritage will not automatically give you new or different skills than the ones you will get through your occupation, but it will give you credible access to your father's skills as elective or secondary skills at the G.M.'s discretion.

Social Status Table

01-05% Vagrant. Your family are vagrants such as itinerant tinkers or the traveling poor – depending on where your campaign is set, this may sometimes mean also belonging to a certain group, like the Irish poor traveling through Elizabethan England or a band of gypsies, going from one small-time employment to the other as day laborers. The financial situation of your family is precarious, you do not have the best reputation (justly or unjustly), but you will know people all around and lots of different places.

06-12% Farmer. Your family is toiling away on the soil. A poor farmer will not even have any right to the land he is working on and own only a very few animals, perhaps not more than a donkey and a goat. A well-to-do farmer will have a legal right to a large area of land where others work for him and will have sundry animals, like a cattle herd.

13-15% Bandit. Running away from the law or fleeing poverty, your family has fled to the forests living by robbery, theft, and poaching. Many such bands were the bane of safe traveling in the 16th and 17th Centuries. A successful bandit may be a dandy highwayman, but most are ragtag rovers and scruffy rogues eking out a meek existence from petty crime.

16-20% Village Official. Your family would perhaps not have a high station in a city, but you do belong to the low gentry, i.e. you are a gentleman. In your village your father has gravitas and is a force to be reckoned with, like a justice of the peace (magistrate) or a mayor.

21-25% Priest. In Elizabethan England your father would likely be an Anglican vicar (although Catholic priest is also possible), but in France, surely a Catholic priest. The latter makes for an automatically more spicy background story. Your family has a solid income and belongs to the well regarded ones in your county.

26-30% Country Squire. Your family belongs to the landed gentry. In all likelihood you do not have to work to make a living. Your income comes from farmers working your land. Good schooling is part of your upbringing.

31-34% Schoolmaster. Your father's a schoolmaster, perhaps even a head master. Maybe he works only in a small country school, maybe a (former) cloister school, but he might also work in one of the prestigious public (private) schools, like the independent boarding schools Charterhouse, Eton, Harrow, Rugby, Shrewsbury, Westminster and Winchester. This gives you easy access to a solid education.

35-38% Learned Doctor. Your father is a learned doctor, i.e. either of philosophy (including a smattering of what we think of as natural sciences today), theology, law, or medicine. He might be employed at a court, work in a university, or serve a certain area. In all cases, he will enjoy the respect and admiration of his clientele and peers.

39-43% Sell Sword. Your father is a mercenary, selling his sword to the highest bidder. He was often absent and fought in many campaigns. Many sell swords return grievously wounded, but a very few are hale and rich by the loot they took, perhaps even leading a peaceful and comfortable country life.

44-47% Sergeant. Much like the sell sword, but with a better social station and a set loyalty to his captain.

48-50% Sailor. Your father is a simple sailor, often away from home for long periods, but he knows the world and hardship.

51-55% Sea Captain. Like the sailor, but leading to a respectable, sometimes even wealthy lifestyle for your family.

56-65% Craftsman. The lifeblood of the cities are its guilds and trades. Your family has a long tradition or working in their trade. Not all crafts are loved, like tanners, but many are respected and honestly paid.

66-68% Artist. Your father is an artist. He may be a sculptor, painter or playwright. He will be well-known 30% of the time.

69-72% Officer (soldier). Your father is a ranking officer in a noble's or the crown's service, leading to a respectable, sometimes even well to do lifestyle for your family.

73-75% Rogue. Your father is a rogue. Perhaps a cardsharp working the better society, a smuggler, a dashing highwayman, or a daring burglar. His life is dangerous but brings sometimes even good income to your family, which may live respectably and the father's true trade may be unknown where you grew up.

76-79% Clerk. From the Elizabethan age onwards, civil service and bureaucracy grew and its clerks became more and more important. Your father may even be highly placed (30%) and have an influential role, one of the so-called noblesse de robe.

80-84% Courtier. Some courtiers are effeminate sycophants, others are movers and shakers. All live and breathe intrigue, vying for the monarch's attention and friendship to gain but risking his sometimes lethal displeasure: like moths getting too close to the flame. Your family is well-to-do; 50% chance of being on the rise, 50% of being close to falling.

85-89% Merchant. Money makes the world go round. It is an age of discovery and wide ranging for strange and foreign goods and the time when England's wealth from wool started.

Being a merchant in this day and age is being on the cusp of great opportunity in very volatile markets. Your family is wealthy (for now).

90-92% Bishop. Your father is one of the princes of the church and as long as the bishop is Anglican, your upbringing was also without scandal.

93-95% New Man (new nobility). Your family rose to its current rich heights in the reign of Henry VIII or later. Your father works hard to retain the monarch's pleasure or he may be engaged in a dangerous intrigue against her.

96-98% Old Nobility. Your family is from the old stock, perhaps even going as far back as 1066 (unlikely but possible to go back farther, as over 90% of the Anglo-Saxon nobility perished on the day their de facto last king, Harold, died). Your family may be wealthy (01-60%), getting by (61-80%), or be destitute and trying hard to regain the status "you deserve" (81-100%).

99-00% Royalty. Your family is somehow related to the monarch and you are, if perhaps remote, in the line of succession. Money is not a problem you know.

Family Background: Odd or Even?

If you want to spice it up a bit more, an even roll in the above *Social Status Table* will mean all is well and square: the character is a legitimate child and the parents are alive and, according to station, well to do. An odd roll, however, will mean the character was born under more interesting circumstances: he may have been born out of wedlock and may *or* may not have been acknowledged by his father *or* at least one parent may be dead (player choice). The latter may mean that the character has inherited something or that the family is in dire straits (if the father died) or that the mother has remarried (G.M. choice). Make an interesting character story! Some drama at the beginning may be an additional motivation why the character wants to make it in the world. Perhaps the parents were killed by bandits or a greedy noble. Maybe the parents were falsely accused of a crime, maybe they had to go into hiding as they were branded as heretics, etc.

Connections

Connections and a personal network are always important, but especially in Elizabethan times, they were not only handy but often decisive for whether you became made and went up the social ladder at all. Also, having a friend who will hide you from the authorities, or other enemies, can save you from being unmade. Having a friend in high places may easily save you from the gallows or let a judge decide the crime was committed by a "certaine Jock-up-Stock" instead of you in full face of evidence to the contrary. In a time when the most peculiar infringements could send you to the gibbet or a public whipping tied to the pillory, being well connected is an advantage you want to have. Well, and then a connection may also "simply" get funds or equipment your way if you know how to ask right. **Each character will start with 1-3 (roll D3) connections.** The connections may be above or below your social

station; require the players to develop a short story where the connection comes from and how close (and why) the character and the connection are. I suggest incentivizing such write-ups if done well by making them worth 50-100 Experience Points each. Connections will spice up your adventures a lot.

Connections Table

01-04% Farmer. You know a farmer. This may be handy when food is scarce in the city or when you need a place to hide.

05-10% Musician. Musicians usually travel a lot. They see places and hear rumors. A good source of information. A musician may even have friends in high places and may be able to give you a leg up.

11-15% Magistrate. It never hurts to know a judge.

16-20% Church Warden. Church wardens enforce church rules in Elizabethan England, e.g. there was a fine if one did not attend service. A church warden usually knows his area well and who is less than attentive at church. He might let a friend slip the church duties or warn him of prosecution.

21-25% Highwayman. Not the most glorious connection, but handy with a sword and a good man to steal a horse with.

26-30% Village Priest. Priests know things and a church is a sacrosanct shelter.

31-38% Innkeeper. Innkeepers hear a lot and will always have a meal and a room for a friend.

39-41% Beggar. A beggar will hardly be able to offer you riches, but beggars often go unnoticed and become privy to overheard information, know the seedier side of town, and where to find a safe spot for the night.

42-47% Sword for Hire. A mercenary such as this can offer you helpful violence, or may have his own contacts he may be willing to either use for you or recommend you to.

48-50% Doxie. A working girl hears a lot and knows her way around town.

51-55% Fence. A good contact to drop contraband or to acquire whatever you may need, for a price. Being friends with a fence may even get you a better price.

56-59% Lawyer. In a pinch, having legal advice and representation at your fingertips is extremely helpful.

60-64% Executioner/Gaoler. Not a glamorous contact, but, who knows, you may be happy to have a friend who leaves the door open for you – to get away just in time.

65-69% Playwright. Playwrights made the Elizabethan age famous. The good ones work in companies sponsored by high ranking nobles or even royalty. Such may give you wonderful connections by proxy or, at least, a place to hide or fashion a couplet for you to help you to convince a lady of your love.

70-74% Weaponsmith or Gunsmith. It never hurts to know a craftsman like this.

75-76% Physician. A doctor who likes you may actually help you. A great connection in an age of ready violence.

77-78% Thief. A thief knows the underbelly of the city or region, he knows where to fence, where to hide, and a lot of things that may come in handy.

79-80% Merchant. A good connection to get some financial help, albeit for a consideration.

81-83% Clerk. In an age where bureaucracy started to grow and civil servants went to places of high regard, to a point where they were known as the "noblesse de robes," a clerk is a very valuable and perhaps even powerful contact.

84-87% New Man. Your contact is one of the "new men," the new nobility elevated to this status recently, probably due to service to Henry VIII or Elizabeth I herself. This contact may be eager for further advancement. Knowing him is helpful, but also perilous.

88-89% Bishop. Powerful friends may be demanding, but they can help you with a word.

90-93% Noble. Your contact is one of the old and powerful hereditary nobility, an earl or duke. A man with his very own agenda, probably playing very high stake games of power and intrigue.

94-95% Lord of the Star Chamber. You contact is part of the select inner circle of Queen Elizabeth, essentially a member of the government. A contact does not get much more influential *and* dangerous.

96-97% Archbishop of Canterbury.

98-99% Lord Cecil or Walsingham (1580s game)/Buckingham (1622 game).

00% Queen Elizabeth I/King James I.

Quality

Each connection will have a *quality*. **Roll 1D10** to determine how powerful, influential, and/or rich the connection will be. For the top four results (Lord of the Star Chamber and higher), this is pretty clear without the roll; each of these will automatically have a quality of 10.

Affection

Each connection will have a measure of *Affection* for the player's character. **Roll 1D10**, the higher the roll, the more affectionate the relationship is between the connection and the character. Affection is the measure of how readily the connection will help and bring his power, influence, and means to bear in favor of the character! The affection value will change in the course of gaming. If the connection is abused or mistreated by the character or has any other bad experience with the character, affection will go down; the worse the character maltreats the connection the more affection will plummet. When affection hits 0 the connection will no longer do anything for the character, and if affection turns negative, the connection will become an enemy and seek redress, even revenge, and may conspire against the character. I suggest for the G.M. to determine affection, keep the development of the score secret, and only describe the effects as they unfold. The development of the relationship will be an important part of the game: role-play it! Elizabethan England and Richelieu France were all about connections.

Cinematic Swashbuckling!

This is a wonderful adventure option and may be played with or without the horror theme. Without the horror, you can still and easily use the BtS Rules but let all characters be of the *Ordinary Person O.C.C.* O.C.C. plus occupation will give you a rounded character. To make matters yet a bit more swashbuckly, I recommend to use the following Stunt Rule, which by the way can be used for any game that you want to make more cinematic. In any BtS game, Stunt Points are an interesting way to spice up the Ordinary Person O.C.C.

Stunt Rule

Use the Ordinary Person O.C.C.'s Potential Psychic Energy points as *Stunt Points*. Stunt Points let you pull, well, awesome stunts. A stunt point can be spent on any action that is not a Strike/Parry/Dodge and requires a skill roll or small sequence of skill rolls to get an automatic success. For example, with a Stunt Point you can jump from one running coach to another with an automatic success. Likewise, if you fall out of a window you can acrobatically swing from balcony to balcony or slow your fall by falling/jumping from marquise to marquise. What works with 1 Stunt Point or requires more than 1 Stunt Point is always G.M. discretion! Think about the acrobatic, dangerous stunts you have seen courtesy of Hollywood from the days of Errol Flynn and Burt Lancaster (Robin Hood, The Crimson Pirate, etc.) to Indiana Jones. Contrary to how P.P.E. normally regenerate, Stunt Points regenerate at the end of the adventure or, when the adventure is particularly long, at the end of each chapter (G.M. decision!).

P.C.C. Restrictions

Almost all P.C.C.s are well suited for transplanting them from our age to the era of Flashing Blades of Horror.

The **Psi-Mechanic** does not immediately strike me as fitting the Renaissance but *could* be used and played as a kind of psionically gifted smith, like a gunsmith, or a "weird" Renaissance inventor like Leonardo da Vinci. If the G.M. allows this, I suggest to encourage players to not merely emulate the technology of today but to think "da Vinci" all the time – e.g., check what the great inventor sketched and work from there. Aspire to be unusual.

The **Ghost Hunter** needs to be adapted slightly so that he only has weapons fitting the 16th or 17th Century, wherever you set your game, but works great. His Devil Sword would probably be a rapier or hand-and-a-half, the Ecto Slayer Shotgun would look like a blunderbuss and the ghost gun would, of course, have a wheellock etc. mechanism and looks. The Ghost Armor is actually easier to wear in an age where armor is still worn regularly. The Ghost Vision Goggles are also no problem as glasses were already around in the 16th Century.

The **Parapsychologist** would be a university don, probably from Oxford or Cambridge, or could be a Nostradamus/Doctor Dee type.

Adapting Core Book Occupations

You can use most occupations from the **Beyond the Supernatural**™ and **Dead Reign**® core books. Naturally, some of the occupation names or themes do not fit perfectly. For example, there was no police force, at least not how we understand it, in the 16th and 17th Century, but the police occupations are for the larger part a great fit for soldierly occupations with a little adapting on the skill set.

For any existing occupation that you want to adapt, strike the skills that do not fit the Flashing Blades of Horror era setting and either supplant them with a skill more fitting (for example: Automobile +20 would become Horsemanship: General +20) or give a like number of free occupational or elective skill picks (for example: striking three skills would give three free skill picks, which you may or may not link to certain skill groups). It is really easy and can be done on the fly.

For Example: **Farmer**. The occupation can be used just as laid out in the *Dead Reign® RPG* (page 91) with only two small changes. The character has Drive Coach (+12%) instead of the "Truck" skill and W.P. Spear instead of W.P. Shotgun. Easy!

New Occupations

01-16% Actor/Playwright. *"The many nights when you could not keep the quill from penning the latest piece – line for line, straight from your heart, even if you stole the story from a Greek tragedy. When you handed it to your fellow actors from your troupe, nervous how it would be received by your patron and the audience. And then, the roaring applause. The tears, the laughter, the raucous celebrations. Full is the cup of life and poor those who never drink from it!"*

Actor was, of course, not a new profession in the Elizabethan age, but one that changed massively. Before the reign of Elizabeth I of England, actors usually only played in regional religious plays. Then the art truly took off, starting with London. Elizabeth loved secular plays. Demand for new plays, and thus for playwrights, went ballistic. Companies of actors formed and were always in search for a patron. The higher nobility eagerly took this up as the fame of the art rubbed off on them. Hence, Shakespeare, for example, was actor, writer, and part owner of the "Lord Chamberlain's" and later, the "King's" Men. Elizabeth's general and public patronage, the money and protection by the noble patrons, and the sheer popularity with all, ranked high or low, made actors famous, not Hollywood level fame but a good actor certainly had access to the upper crust. This continued in England unbroken but for the more restrictive reign of Oliver Cromwell. The Stuarts loved the arts just as much as Elizabeth I had. Definitely a profession with a future and promising connections, if not with a steady income.

Occupational Skills: Creative Writing (+25), Fencing, Gymnastics (+10%), Hand to Hand: Basic, History (+10%), Impersonation (+10%), Lore: Mythology (+5%), Performance (+25%), Streetwise (+15%), Wardrobe & Grooming (+20%), W.P. Sword.

Elective Skills: Select six from the standard available categories plus from any Espionage and Rogue skills.

Secondary Skills Available: Select four from the standard available categories at level one, +1 additional skill at levels 3, 6, 9, and 12.

Special Bonus: Even as a non-psychic and notwithstanding any limits of his P.C.C./O.C.C. (Ordinary Person O.C.C., for example, normally has no I.S.P.), receives +1D6 I.S.P. and the Total Recall psionic power (BtS-II core book, page 128).

Advantages: Access to higher circles of society despite any social rank the actor may have been born with, and the potential to become famous. The character hears a lot of gossip. Most know the seedy side of town as well as the upper circles. With his artist's sensibility and knowledge of myths, he will be more ready to accept the rumors and signs of supernatural activity he will catch wind of.

Disadvantages: Aside from the wobbly pay, actors and playwrights spend most of their time with their troupe. Playwrights usually have a haunt – on the cheap side (in London, probably quite literally) for many, on the posh side for a few – where they tend to meet other playwrights and enjoy life to the hilt.

Pay: 01-10% Fallen on Hard Times, two pence per day (alms level, about 3 pounds per year). 11-80% Part of a Troupe, 10 pounds per year. 81-100% A Rising Star, 100 pounds per year as long as fame and fortune last.

17-34% Clergyman. *"After so many years of training for the church and serving the Lord, you are no longer sure if it was the call from on high or your father sending you to a decent profession with humble income but good reputation for the family. Some of your fellows are thin on their theology but strong in their will for influence. You, no, you just do as your conscience and faith will you forth. The line to heaven is never straight, but all's in a day's work and should be seemly."* A clergyman is a part of a church. In Tudor and Stuart England this will usually be either the Church of England (Anglican) or the Catholic Church or a more protestant streak. Most clergymen in the, more or less, established two churches are officials and have a certain position and function, like the vicar of a parish or one of the canons – for example, the Canon Librarian – of a cathedral. They may also be nuns, monks or even legates (messengers and special officers) from the Pope, especially when they come from continental Europe.

Occupational Skills: Creative Writing (+20%), History (+15%), Language: Other (Latin; spoken; +15%), Literacy: Other Language (Latin; written; +20%), Public Speaking (+20%), Research (+25%), Theology or Lore: Religion (+20%), Wardrobe & Grooming (+10%), two other skills (at +15% each) selected from Paranormal Studies and Science skills, and two more skills selected from Communications,

Espionage, Medical, Paranormal Studies or Science skills or may spend both skill picks to acquire Hand to Hand: Basic.

Elective Skills: Select seven skills from the standard available categories plus Espionage.

Secondary Skills Available: Select two from the standard available categories at levels 1, 3, 7, 11, and 14.

Special Bonus: +10% Charm/Impress.

Advantages: Clergymen tend to be trusted, at least by those from the same denomination, or may be feared depending on the political climate of the time and place. They often have influence and access to those higher placed, be they of the church or secular gentles and lords. A clergyman is usually not asked what is business is in any place and, as a rule, unless in a convent or similar, pretty free in his scheduling for a given day. Clergymen are often called upon, in confidence or openly, to investigate supernatural activities – after all, the realm of spirits, angels and demons is real and the clergy its chief authority. Here it has to be noted, again, that the sensibilities and beliefs of the 16th and 17th Centuries may be not unlike those of today, but renaissance and baroque man did not put the uncanny and weird down to superstition, but to acts of entities beyond the ken of man.

Disadvantages: If the clergyman has a parish it may be hard for him to get away for an extended period.

Pay: A vicar or rector with his own parish will have an annual income of about 30 pounds. A priest without parish will earn considerably less. A bishop will earn between 187 pounds/year (St. Aseph, Wales) to 2,874 pounds/year (Winchester).

35-50% Courtier. The courtier is usually a lady or a gentleman living or working at court. A lady-in-waiting is one example, a court official, like the Lord Admiral Buckingham, another. Some courtiers apparently have no official function at all but seek the attention and favor of an official, a lord or the monarch. Everything around court revolves around the monarch; she is the center of the courtly world. Courtiers are like moths swirling towards the monarch's bright light, some bask in the glow and prosper while others burn and perish. There is a reason Louis XIV would call himself the Sun King later. A courtier collects, buys, deals with, and sometimes forces favors and information – these are the common coin of court, not money. Money is merely the automatic result of position and land; both can be had at court when you have enough leverage to get them. Under all that finery and behind the splendor, the court is the most dangerous snake pit of all. The character strives to be a mover and shaker in that high stakes environment. Be not be fooled by the finery and outwardly graceful conduct of the Courtier – he may dress up like a peacock, but many of them are experienced duelists and cunning schemers.

Occupational Skills: Athletics (General), Court Etiquette (+20%), Dance (+15%), Diplomacy (+20%), Law (+10%), Gambling (Standard) (+10%), Hand to Hand: *Basic* or *Expert*, Horsemanship: General (+10%), Performance (+15%), Public Speaking (+10%), Savoir Vivre (+15%), Wardrobe & Grooming (+30%).

Elective Skills: Select eight skills from the standard available categories plus Espionage *or* Military.

Secondary Skills Available: Select 4 from the standard available categories at levels 1, +1 at level 3, 6, 9, and 12.

Special Bonus: +10% to *one* Occupational Skill.

Advantages: A courtier is free in his scheduling and may come and go as he pleases, unless his obligations keep him at court. He has (potential) access to the high and mighty and the important functionaries of court.

Disadvantages: A courtier does not get any payment per se. He is subject to the whims of the monarch and rumors against the character may prove to be just as lethal as a dagger in the back, which may also happen.

Pay: Varies highly. Roll percentile to see his current amount of savings in pounds. Now roll 2D10 a second time; if you roll doubles, the character will have a royal stipend of 50 pounds per year and a court function of the G.M.'s choice.

51-66% Freebooter. *"Ah, nothing like the sound of the sails unfurling, the wind in your back, and the smell of the salty sea in your nose. By Her Majesty's leave, off to adventure, fortune, and fame, a royal warrant in your pocket. Anchor away, onward, ho!"* Sir Francis Drake, Walter Raleigh, etc., famous by their daring exploits on sea and land, are the archetypal freebooters, classic adventurers. A freebooter will go and do boldly what other men only dream of, or fear. Some are reckless, some less than honorable, but most make a point of being dashing and show panache, and all are in it, to win it: the favor of the monarch and a royal bounty.

Occupational Skills: Boat: Sail Types (+30%), Boats: Ships/Seamanship (+20%), Climb (+20%), Fencing, Hand to Hand: Expert, Language: Other (+8%), Lore: Superstitions (+5%), Navigation (+15%), Physical Labor, Rope Works (+10%), Witty Repartee (+10%), W.P. Sword and 2 other W.P.s of choice.

Elective Skills: Select seven; can make selections from the standard available categories and/or from Rogue skills.

Secondary Skills Available: Select 2 from the standard available categories at level one, +1 additional skill at levels 2, 4, 6, 9, and 12.

Special Bonus: +2 to save vs Horror Factor.

Advantages: The character sees and hears a lot, traveling far and wide over the seven seas. He will catch wind of the strangest tales and rumors of magic, artifacts, and the supernatural going bump throughout the world. The dashing Freebooter is admired by many and people love hearing the tales of his exploits, which he likes to share.

Disadvantages: Flamboyance has its upside, but on the downside, the Freebooter tends to be outstandingly visible, which does not lend itself well to covert work.

Pay: Varies highly. Roll 1D100 to see his current amount of savings in pounds. The higher you roll, the more famous was the character's last exploit. Future income will depend on the next catch he makes or mission he takes.

67-83% Dandy Highwayman. *"I have the freedom of the road. I can go wherever I please and do whatever I want. If I want something, I will take it. If needs be, by force. Stand and* *deliver! Now, be a darling, and hand over that bracelet – it is worth only money, but its color hardly suits her ladyship's beautiful eyes."* Fierce in his passions, calm in the execution of the most daring stunts, the Dandy Highwayman keeps the roads unsafe and his life a series of dangerous exploits. Naturally, he is after the next catch, but what he really seeks is the thrill of adventure. He would enjoy breaking into a castle just as much as seducing an Earl's daughter. There are none above his station and laws are too tight to hold him. Some Highwaymen have a deeper secret – they may have become Highwaymen only as the best means to gain funds as a first step, but are really out to avenge a past wrong or to regain their family's lost standing.

Occupational Skills: Acrobatics (+10%), Detect Ambush (+10%), Disguise (+15%), Escape Artist (+15%), Fencing, Find Contraband (+20%), Hand to Hand: Expert, Horsemanship: Elite (+10%), Roadwise (+20%), Wardrobe & Grooming (+15%), Wilderness Survival (+10%), W.P. Black Powder Weapons, W.P. Sword, W.P. Trick Shooting.

Elective Skills: Select six; can make selections from the standard available categories and/or from Rogue skills.

Secondary Skills Available: Select four from the standard available categories at level one, +1 additional skill at levels 3, 6, 9, and 12.

Special Bonus: +2 to strike on either W.P. Black Powder Weapons or on hand to hand W.P.s, +2 Roll with Impact.

Advantages: The character gets around and hears a lot of stories on the road and in the inns and towns he will come through and stay for a while. He catches lots of odd tales and the many legends and myths, mostly dark tales of dread around old cairns, hills, and the dark woods, of the countryside.

Disadvantages: The Highwayman is always a wanted man from the day he starts his "trade." That said, in a time before CCTV and without good communication beyond shouting distance, that does not mean that someone is right on his heels or that he has to fear being recognized by just anyone right away. However, someone might be very put out by having been robbed and send out his henchmen or hired thugs to find the offender.

Pay: Varies. Roll 1D100 to see his current amount of savings in shillings (1/12th of a pound). The higher you roll, the more infamous was the character's last exploit. Future income will depend on the next catch he makes or mission he takes.

84-00% Gentleman Soldier/Musketeer. *"Fight hard, feast like it is your last day, but never lose your eye for beauty. That's what I say. The day is mine ... but my life belongs to the crown. For the honor of the King and for the glory of the realm!"* Just think The Three Musketeers or The Flashing Blade and you have the best possible picture in mind. The Gentleman Soldier is mostly self-funded in his service for the crown. It could be said, in that as well as in the strict observance of a gentlemanly code of conduct, the Gentleman Soldier is the true heir of medieval knighthood. The most eponymous Gentleman Soldier is, of course, the French musketeer. The musketeer was a prestigious military specialist profession, starting in the age of Richelieu France, where the first musketeer unit was created in 1622 – all musketeers had to be "gentlemen," i.e. of noble birth, and pay for their uniform and most of their equipment themselves. Yet, the archetype was present throughout the era covered here. In Elizabethan England, there was no standing army for the most part. It is believed that Elizabeth had no more than 2,000 or 3,000 men at her permanent disposal. The Elizabethan Gentleman Soldier would be either "Queen's man," perhaps a courtier even, or a well-trained militiaman of some great lord's retinue. In the Stuart age, the character would be an adventurously minded gentleman of means (as firearms are then still quite expensive) or a cavalier!

Occupational Skills: Acrobatics (+10%), Fencing, Forced March, Gambling (+15%), Hand to Hand: Martial Arts, Horsemanship: General (+10%), Law (General) or Streetwise (either at +10%), Military Etiquette (+20%), Savoir Vivre (+20%), Wardrobe & Grooming (+10%), Witty Repartee (+10%), W.P. Black Powder Weapons, W.P. Knife, W.P. Sword, W.P. Trick Fencing.

Elective Skills: Select seven from the standard available categories and/or from Military and Rogue skills.

Secondary Skills Available: Select two from the standard available categories at level one, +1 additional skill at levels 3, 6, 9, and 12.

Special Bonus: +2 strike with fencing *and* black powder weapons, +1 Initiative.

Advantages: Gentlemen Soldiers, especially when they have a formalized social status, like the French Musketeers, are known for their allegiance, loyalty, fighting prowess, and strict code of honor. They are respected as fencers and that they do not react leniently to insults. For a famous Gentleman Soldier this may mean that his name carries weight. When a well-known fencer only puts his hand on the hilt of his rapier, most other men will take a step back and apologize.

Disadvantages: Fame invites envy, envy breeds insults, honor demands redress – you may have a fair amount of fights ahead of you... If you want to call that a disadvantage, Sir?!

Pay: Varies, but will mostly have to rely on his own funds and the occasional grant from his/her Majesty. His funds will be: 01-30% meager (probably from an impoverished noble family not unlike a certain D'Artagnan; 3 pounds, a simple set of the minimum equipment for a gentleman soldier and the clothes on his back), 31-70% moderate (an annual stipend from his family of 25 pounds and a full set of good equipment, including a choice of clothing adequate to his gentlemanly standing), 71-100% well-to-do (probably from a well situated or even powerful noble family, and might even have a title above a knighthood himself, with an annual income from land of 200 pounds).

Money

Money makes the world go round, they say. Your players will want to know what kind of funds they have and what they can buy with it.

Elizabethan & Stuart Currency

In Elizabethan England there was no paper money, unless you count bonds (essentially, debt letters that could be traded) and the staple coins were, like today, the pound and the penny. However, there was (I) a wild assortment of coins around, which we do not see anymore these days, (ii) the pound had 240 pennies to it and not 100 as today, and (iii) 1 pound worth bought far, far more than a pound sterling can buy today. Note, however, that before the year 1583 things were counted in pounds but the pound as a coin did not exist yet. Likewise, the Mark was also not minted in England, but was a value – worth 180 pennies – used for accounting, land deeds, dowry determinations, etc. in Elizabethan times. All coins are either silver or gold, copper coins were not used before 1797. The famous English Guinea gold coin was not minted before 1663, it was then the first machine struck coin. Sir Isaac Newton worked in a royal mint and actually developed minting machinery. All the coins below are hand-struck. The coins varied in size and weight over the years and from reign to reign – sometimes they also weighed less because of clipping, i.e. cutting or filing off gold or silver from the coin's edges – so that any weights and sizes given are approximations, but you will find the following "standard" coins:

Gold Coins

The gold coins have diverse faces, most notably the three great coins, sovereign, royal, and angel.

Sovereign: Rather beautiful gold coin, the Elizabethan "pound" – the pound is abbreviated "L" or "£" for libra, the Latin word for pound weight. The coin is minted with the face of the monarch – hence, the name – on one side and the royal arms of England on the reverse. It is almost 100% pure gold. Size/Weight: 15.6 grams, 1.73 inches (44 mm). Value: 240 pennies (occasionally, you will still find the "Fine Sovereign," also known as the "double-noble," struck in 1550 with a value of 360 pennies!).

Royal: Gold coin, also referred to as the "rose noble" as it shows the Tudor rose on one side and a ship with a rose on the reverse, was introduced by Mary Tudor and struck again by Elizabeth I between 1584 and 1589, mainly to finance her actions in the Netherlands. Size/Weight: 15.6 grams, 1.73 inches (44 mm). Value: 180 pennies (Royals from before Queen Mary only had a value of 120 pennies).

Angel: Most common gold coin used. The Archangel Michael slaying a dragon is depicted on this coin – hence, the name. Size/Weight: 2.6 grams, c. 0.79 inches (20 mm). Value: 120 pennies.

Crown: Very common gold or silver coin, but both are actually each worth the same. This coin was also widely held to be of equal value to the French Êcu (which Shakespeare has called the "French Crown"), the Venetian Ducat, and a Flemish Gelder. The Crown shows the face of the monarch on one side, and the English coat of arms on the reverse. Size/Weight: 30 grams, 1.73 inches (44 mm). Value: 60 pennies.

Half Crown: Gold coin. Like the Crown, this coin shows the face of the monarch on one side, and the English coat of arms on the reverse. Size/Weight: 15 grams, c. 1.38 inches (35 mm). Value: 30 pennies.

Silver Coins

All of the silver coins show the face of the monarch on one side and the English coat of arms on the reverse.

Shilling (originally called "Testoon"): Silver coin, abbreviated "s" for the Latin word "sestertius." Rare and not popular in the first part of the 16th Century, but became the dominant coin in circulation starting at the end of the 16th Century. Size/Weight: 5.6 grams, 1.18 inches (30 mm). Value: 12 pennies.

Groat (sometimes called Fourpence): Silver coin, issued since the reign of Henry VIII. Size/Weight: 2.5 grams, 0.98 inches (25 mm). Value: 4 pennies.

Tuppence (sometimes referred to as a Half Groat): Silver coin worth 2 pence. Value: 2 pence.

Penny: Silver coin, abbreviated "d" for the Latin word "denarius." Value: 1 pence.

Ha'penny: Silver coin worth half a penny. Value: ½ pence.

Farthing: Silver quarter penny fragment, not used since the Elizabethan times, but may be left over in circulation from the middle ages. Value: ¼ pence.

Purchasing Power

According to http://www.measuringworth.com/ppoweruk/ the relative value of 1 pound in 1588 is equal to about 322 US Dollars of today. For simplicity's sake, in order to quickly find the value of goods, you would divide today's dollar prices by 320 (ratio £ 1 in 1588 to 257.50 GBP in 2016 to $321.56 USD as of the day of writing this). **Quick and dirty conversion:** As you will happily note from the above, £ 1 in Elizabethan times had 240 pennies to it, so you could alternatively convert quickly and dirtily by translating each US Dollar to 1 Elizabethan penny! This is anything but totally exact or historically accurate but it will work, too. Either method will help you give away appropriate rewards to the players, determine "treasure size," and find prices for goods and services on the fly without holding up the game.

Prices for Some Choice Items

Arms and Armor: Black Powder Weapons: A pistol will be 12s to 30s, a musket may cost up to 40s. These are the basic prices for the most easily available weapons of the time. That will usually be a matchlock. A flintlock will cost at least double the amount, the wheellock is even a bit more expensive. The flintlock may not be easily available if you play before 1600. If you want the same weapon rifled (extremely rare; who needs such newfangled nonsense) or of quality or, as many gentleman will insist, with beautiful wood and silverwork ornaments, prices can go up further still. Black powder is 7d/pound. Melee Weapons: A rapier will be about 10s, but again with beautiful work done on the hilt and cross-guard, perhaps some ornamental etchings on the blade, but it can be far more expensive in the end – as a rule of thumb, up to about 4-5 pounds for an exquisite weapon that will make nobody at court turn away from the poor country squire. A pike will cost only about 2s.

Clothing: Prices for clothing are highly varied and depend on what material (leather, various types of cloth) you use and which dyes. To give some examples: A courtier's fine breeches could be had for 7 pounds and a good shirt would cost 1 pound. A good pair of boots would be 4-10 pounds, but a simple pair of shoes for a peasant would probably be no more than 1-2s. A soldier's coat would be about 8 pounds. As you can see, while 1 set of clothing per year is not such a great salary part to us, it was valuable to the employed lower class.

Food: A tankard of beer at a tavern will be a ha'penny, 2/3 of a gallon to take home will be 1 penny only, and a bottle of some French wine is 2s – it often had to be smuggled. A simple meal at a pub is 1-2 pence, a capon will be about 2s. A loaf of bread is 2d, a bushel of oysters 4d, 300 herrings 3s, a chicken only 1d.

Lodging: To lodge at an inn will cost you 2d/week (common room) or 6d/week in a feather bed (probably for yourself). To lease a modest farm would be 4-5 pounds a year, a rich farm feeding more than just your family (in a normal to good year) and providing income would easily set you back 50 pounds a year.

Miscellaneous: Going to the theater is 1 penny (standing in the pits) to 6-12 pence for a separate room to watch. Having a smoke can be expensive for roughly 12s to the pound of tobacco. A pack of playing cards is 2d. Taking the coach from Dover to London is 3s.

Income

Income is a "natural" corrective for the purchasing power conversion. As you will have seen, I have given some incomes for the Elizabethan occupations above, but to give you a more rounded idea of what people earn, here is an overview:

On the lowest rung: 2d/day is alms level and roughly £ 3 a year. A servant would rate about double that amount, but would also be clothed.

With a trade: A craftsman apprentice will often not even earn as much, but will have board, lodging, and 1 new set of clothes a year, and, most valuably, be taught. Very different from today, many masters back in the day would *ask* for payment to accept an apprentice. A journeyman can expect to earn about 6d/day (£ 9 per year) and a master 8d/day (£ 12 per year). Depending on the trade and the current market demand for such a trade, the daily earnings could go up or down by about 50%. Soldiers and sailors would earn similar, albeit usually a little lower, wages as journeymen and masters.

Clergy: A vicar or rector with a parish will earn about £ 30 per year and have a house for his use. A bishop's annual earnings are £ 180-2,900; the richest see is the Bishopric of Winchester, closely followed by the most powerful see in the realm: the Archdiocese of Canterbury.

Gentry: It has been said at the time that you need to earn £ 300 a year from land to call yourself a gentleman in the north of England and £ 500 in the south, but this was an exaggerated figure. Most gentlemen will earn about £ 100 a year

in net revenue from their lands. A gentleman does not need to be knighted, but he is addressed with the honorary title of Esquire. Fun anecdote: When you are in debt with an English bank, the letter reminding you to balance your account will be addressed to [your name], Esq., because as you are in debt, the bank assumes you must be a gentleman. Gentlemen often were indebted to moneylenders and banks for several months in a row as their income from their land would only pay out twice per year around harvest times. A rich gentleman may earn about £ 2,000 per year.

Merchants: Merchants can be wildly rich, but while eager to display their status and wealth, would usually not be assumed gentlemen. You must have land to be part of the gentry. A shopkeeper would earn about £ 30 a year; well-to-do wool merchants would make about £ 500 a year. The richest London Aldermen commanded an income of around £ 6,000 per year, more than most high ranking nobles. Even then London was the center of commerce in England. The most wealthy merchant at the end of the reign of Elizabeth I had an income of *at least* £ 12,000!

Nobility: Nobles like barons will have an income of often under £ 200 per year and several members of the gentry were better off, but held lower status, and some barons had an income of around £ 1,000. Income, as with the gentry, is usually proportionate to the amount of land a person holds. The more, the wealthier. Consequently, the Crown, followed by the Church of England and the Universities of Oxford and Cambridge, are the wealthiest persons/bodies in the realm as they hold the most land directly. A peer like an earl, unless impoverished for whatever reason, especially when his lands have been taken away from him, which happened more often than one might assume, will command an income of about £ 2,000-5,000 per year. The income of the Queen/King is not known, but the annual cost to maintain the palaces and other property of Elizabeth I was about £ 220,000 per year. That is about as much as the total income of the gentry of all of England combined.

Adventures: Hook, Line, & Sinkers™

"For the Honor of the King!"

Can be set well in 1622 or need some adjustments.

Hook: George Villiers calls on you! Out of curiosity about what opportunity lies in store for you, and perhaps a tiny bit out of fear (or prudent caution, if you prefer to call your heart suddenly beating a little harder that), you gracefully confirm. Nobody in his right mind denies an invitation from the good Marquess of Buckingham, Lord Admiral of the Fleet and very close counselor to His Majesty, King James I. You have heard rumors, of course. This is the Royal Court after all! Maybe this has to do with the unrest caused by King James dissolving parliament a few days earlier. There was talk approaching treason yesterday by some very put out men when you were at the dice at the ale house. You remember this with a smile as you stuffed the slur right back into those men's mouths before they could say too much. You probably saved them from hanging or worse and got a little exercise out of it, not that those merchants gave much sport. They should thank you. But then, maybe it has to do with the young rake, the 22 year old Charles, Prince of Wales; Charles fell ill, apparently severely. The cause is not known, but some say that it is the French Disease which he got from his last affair: The Italian Countess, Maria D'Auria of Naples.

Line: The prince is, indeed, severely ill. He is pale, lackluster, and feverish. He looks as if his blood had been drawn from him. This is not the French Disease, this is something strange. The King himself, famous for his book on demon lore, thinks the Prince has been attacked by an "obsession," i.e. a supernatural creature attacking him physically. Hasn't Charles complained that Maria was lately so cold to the touch?

Sinker: The King and Lord Buckingham believe that you must find the Countess, identify if she is a demon, and capture or destroy her. The real Countess has died some weeks ago during her affair with Charles. She was killed by a special form of a Syphon Entity, a Blood Syphon. The Blood Syphon has similar abilities to a Syphon Entity but feeds only through consuming its victim's blood, bit by bit, until it can wait no more and will suck it out entirely, thus killing the host and turning the host body into a zombie-like creature. Use the *Mock Zombie* stats from Dead Reign, but note that the Entity ruling the body is very intelligent and can use its psionic abilities. The (un)dead host body will deteriorate quickly, unless the Blood Syphon can constantly sustain it by feeding on blood from more victims. As the Blood Syphon cannot leave the host body without giving it up completely (it could not re-enter), it can only feed the host body and itself through the mouth of the host body – the "zombie" basically becomes a blood drinker! The Countess has left for her country estate ... a trail of blood-drained victims will lead there. *For more details on the Blood Syphon, see the description of the creature at the end of this article.*

"Royal Act"

Can be set well in 1585 or needs some minor adjustments.

Hook: The party is pressed into service for Walsingham to contact one of his agents in Calais ("*Elizabethan 1588*"; I suggest to set it in 1585) or for Richelieu to contact a French spy in La Rochelle ("*1622 Musketeer*") or for Lord Buckingham and an English spy in Paris ("1622 Stuart").

Line: The spy has uncovered part of a plot. He has not sent any messages for a few days now. The party is to find out if anything happened to him and aid him or carry on his work. When the party arrives in Calais, they find the agent horribly murdered in his room at the "Trois Mouettes" inn. They hear he was ill the last few days and in considerable pain. Nobody disturbed him for long for fear of contracting the horrible disease. A medical doctor, "*a very learned man, English from his accent, arrived yesterday evening and tried but also could not help the poor soul.*" All the papers of the agent are gone.

Sinker: The last contact of the agent was a group of actors. One of the actors is a cultist. The cult plans to get royal blood, the purer the better to summon a demon with it. The Queen's blood may make summoning a demon lord possible. The cultist became aware of the agent snooping around and poisoned him. When the agent was so weak and in fear for his life, the actor disguised himself as an English physician and "tried to help" the agent. He said he could not help, the agent would surely die, but if he could give a message to the agent's family, he would do so as he planned on taking the next ship to England. The agent gave his papers to the "doctor" on the oath that the physician would expedite the papers to England posthaste. When the party questions the innkeeper and staff, one of the serving maids will come up and say that "he was such a handsome man, the doctor, he looked just like Kirk de Plecy, the actor." Kirk de Plecy is, indeed, well known – one of the best actors of his day (fictional, though). When the party follows up on this, they will quickly find the troupe of which de Plecy is part: the Archbishop of Canterbury's Men. The cultist is very wary and alert. If he thinks that the party is after him somehow, he will disguise himself as a French sergeant and inform the royal soldiers that English spies (the party) are loose in the city. This will lead to a chase through the city. The party should (barely) get away or escape prison in an exciting manner. They will then find out that de Plecy and his troupe have taken a ship to England and have an engagement to play for the Queen at Richmond Palace (10 miles up the Thames from London), which will give great opportunities for some court interaction for the characters and very careful actions against de Plecy as even Walsingham does not want to arrest or disappear an actor with such an excellent reputation whom the Queen is keen to see and who is one of the Archbishop's men.

"Bloody Vanity"

Based on a real story. Can be set any time after 1570 or needs some minor adjustments. I suggest setting it in rural England ("Elizabethan 1588," "Stuart Reign 1610") or France ("1622 Musketeers").

Hook: When young women disappear from several small towns, the party is asked (begged, paid, or commanded – depending on set-up) to investigate. No trace of the girls is found.

Line: The women are between the ages of 13 and 25, most around 16-21. In total, over 20 have gone missing in the last several years. The villagers are afraid and believe a horrible creature, perhaps the dark lord himself but surely a demon, is taking their virgin daughters away to still its insatiable hunger for innocence, but its appetite is unquenchable. It must be found and sent back to Hell.

Sinker: Elizabeth Báthory, a Hungarian/Transylvanian princess, has settled in a fine manor in [insert where you want the players to be]. She is the daughter of George IV and is the widow of the Voivode of Transylvania; a Voivode has the social rank of a German Herzog, i.e. a Duke. The locals have heard that: *Lady Elizabeth has left Hungary after the death of her husband, too aggrieved to remain. She maintains a very fine household and throws many parties. She is extremely good-looking. She must be over 40 but looks not a day older than 25; these Hungarian ladies are simply blessed. The duchess is very rich. She has a lot of servants and is wearing such beautiful finery. She buys it in [insert next big city] or sends for it straight from the capital.*

Elizabeth Báthory is a cruel and nefarious alchemist and has found the secret of the elixir of youth (or so she thinks, if you do not want such an elixir to be real). She is actually Anna Báthory, born 1539 and allegedly died in 1570, and is from a powerful Hungarian noble family; you only have to adjust the dates if you play before 1570. It is very unlikely that anyone knows about Anna's background beyond what the people have heard in rumors. Transylvania is in all probability, simply too far away from your game setting and too much of a forlorn "rustic hinterland" that anyone would know the peculiars of the nobles of Hungary, Austria or Poland. She is luring girls and young women to her estate, or sometimes simply has them abducted by her faithful henchmen, and then slowly kills them. She believes, sickly, that blood drained under pain – the more extreme the better – is the most important ingredient of the elixir of youth. She then spices the blood up with a refined herbal essence, some sea salts, a sprinkle of gold, and a dash of brandy; then, she drinks the concoction with the aim to remain perpetually young and alive. It works, kind of. She needs the elixir monthly. If she sits out a month, she grows older by 10 years for each month without feeding. While a Hungarian "princess" is not a French or English noble, the players cannot expect any help from watchmen or the military policing the countryside (in France, the maréchaussée), or any other official. Elizabeth/Anna is untouchable, especially without evidence, and it would need a lot of steel-clad evidence to get her even near any courtroom.

Seed: For some further inspiration you may want to check for the gruesome story of Anna's daughter, Elizabeth Báthory, the "Blood Countess." When the party is successful, this may lead to repercussions from her family, like hired assassins, or further adventures in Transylvania. Anna is a monster, which may be a dark family secret or unknown to her family, but a violent death of one of their own will rile up the Hungarian temper for sure.

"The Beast"

Can be set anywhere, but the area should be rural, mountainous, and off the great roads. The following assumes it is set in the massive central area of 1630 France.

Hook: The party is passing through a village and hears a horrible tale at an inn (or, maybe, they are sent with a royal warrant to investigate). A wolf or pack of wild dogs has been killing people for weeks now. Most victims were killed by having their throat torn out, but they were not eaten.

Line: All killings happened between the onset of dusk and before dawn in an area of roughly 90 by 80 kilometers (56 by 50 miles). *"The victims were mostly women and chil-dren and shepherdesses celebrated for their beauty,* as the villagers report, although in one case, armed horsemen were pursued and in another a mail coach was chased *"in broad noonday, can you believe it?!" "The horsemen could only flee at neck-breaking gallop, which killed one of the two men, but the other lives; the survivor is one of the men of Baron Yves de Fouchard." "The coachmen are alive and well but they lost three of their strongboxes as they threw them at the gigantic grey wolf giving them chase; they will be back in the village soon as they pass through every two weeks on their route between Paris and Clairmont-Ferrand."* The villagers are sure it is a Loup-Garou, a werewolf. The authorities do not officially believe that but think it is a pack of feral dogs or perhaps overgrown grey wolves. They cannot explain, however, how or why dogs or wolves would have opened doors or jumped through a closed window when they killed the Baron's kitchen maid. *"The baron's men and, indeed, all soldiers and watchmen in the area do their best to find and kill the beast but they had no luck so far, it is elusive as a ghost."* As they are all out hunting, there has been more banditry.

Sinker: One year ago a man, Luc Sablé, murdered his wife and children in a fit of drunken rage. He was hung after a very short trial and buried without any blessing in an unmarked grave in a corner of the graveyard of Fouchard. The Baron also holds the office of magistrate and was the judge in the case. The graveyard is on a Celtic holy site and a ley line. The Celtic magic still lingers and unless a person who has committed a mortal sin is buried with the proper rites (of any faith, actually), that person will come back every night as murderous wolf, returning to their grave every night. Luc will be put to rest only when he is decapitated and the head is then thrown into a stream "to wash away the sins." The party may find the latter out with a roll on Lore: Religion (alternatively, Lore: Superstitions or History: General at -20) or by talking to Magda, the local witch, err, midwife and herbalist. Luc takes on the form of a huge wolf when he hunts at night. Use the stats for a normal wolf, even if he has the form of a "man-wolf," but with supernatural strength. He is intelligent, which is why he can open doors as long as they are not locked and have a latch a dog could open. He cannot be killed by normal wounds, they all heal quickly, so jumping through a glass window is nothing that makes Luc shy away from. Luc is not rational but driven by hatred, out on a killing rampage every night. The bandits in the area make best use of the wolf problem and break into houses and steal as much as they can, but they are no murderers.

Seeds: Alternatively, you can of course turn this into a more straightforward werewolf tale or leave out the monster completely, changing the story to be either "just" about normal wolves/feral dogs or about a group of murderous bandits. Read more on the Beast of Gévaudan for further inspiration.

New Monster

Entity: Blood Syphon

The Blood Syphon is related to the Syphon in many ways. Unlike the Syphon, the Blood Syphon can only inhabit living creatures, preferably human beings. The creature needs to convert blood to P.P.E. to stay alive or will fall dormant for 1D100 years; it will awake when a living being passes within 10 yards of it and will try to possess the living being. As the Syphon, the Blood Syphon delights in manipulating, corrupting, and destroying humans, preferably by causing pain to the being. It can communicate with its host and will try to corrupt it that way. It is very creative in finding the right "buttons" to push with any human. It almost always manages to lure its host away from the right path into evilness and to share in its plans. The Blood Syphon takes great delight from conning a human into believing that the bad deeds are actually good or even divine. The Blood Syphon is less patient than the Syphon. It is perpetually hungry and very aware that insufficient nourishment will cause it to slither away into unconsciousness with a very high risk of passing away into mindless eternity. Its greatest weakness is that its very impatience invariably leads to the Blood Syphon draining all blood from its host, turning the host into a kind of zombie.

Also known as the: *Bloodsucker, Wiederganger.*

Alignment: Diabolic (Evil).

Attributes: Not applicable. Very cunning and utterly ruthless, equal to an I.Q. of 18 (reduced to an equivalent of 6 if *starving*), and is an invisible and intangible energy being.

Armor Rating (A.R.): None in energy form, or as per the A.R. of the host.

Hit Points: 10D6+12

S.D.C.: None.

Discorporation: Only people who can see the invisible or spirits can see the Blood Syphon, an elegantly formed butterfly with human eyes and blood red mists swirling in its gossamer-edged wings. When destroyed, they explode in a puff of light and leave a splash of stinking blood covering a 10 foot (3 m) diameter area.

Average Life Span: Immortal until destroyed or fading due to lack of sustenance.

Threat Level: x6; Haunter.

Horror Factor: 10; 12 when in a zombie host; 14 when its trail of blood drained victims is known and leads to the entity.

Size: 10 inches (25 cm) tall.

Weight: Not applicable for an energy being.

P.P.E.: 2D6

Natural Abilities: In energy form the Entity can hover and fly at a maximum speed of 30 mph (48 km) and is intangible. The Blood Syphon is a natural Telepath, i.e it can use the Telepathy psionic power without having to spend I.S.P. It understands all languages at 100%, but cannot read. Unlike the Syphon, it is not able to possess inanimate objects but only living creatures who get a save vs possession to resist.

It can control one person or, when the Blood Syphon has drained and thereby killed the human, control the remaining (zombie) host body.

The host body has **all** the stats, abilities, and vulnerabilities of a *Mock Zombie* (**Dead Reign® RPG**, page 51), but that people slain by a Blood Syphon host body do not rise as zombies themselves – the victims of the victim, so to speak, are simply dead. The host body is considered properly destroyed only if (a) decapitated or (b) completely destroyed (burnt or dissolved in acid for example). While controlling a host body, the Blood Syphon can use all of its psionic abilities.

Vulnerabilities: Cannot read, unless its host can. The creature must absorb at least 1 P.P.E. every 3 days or will perish. All magic and psionic attacks. Impervious to physical attacks, energy, gases, drugs, poison, cold, heat, fire, disease and most everything that can harm a physical being when in energy form. When possessing a human being it can leave the being at any time, but only if it takes 2 full rounds without any other actions of both the host and the Blood Syphon to drain its victim completely. The Blood Syphon is compelled to "eat up." When the Blood Syphon leaves the host body, which may also happen if the host is properly destroyed, it cannot immediately possess the next living being, but has to wait for 1D6 days to re-adjust to its energy existence first.

R.C.C. Skills or Equivalents (do not improve with experience): None, communicates via Telepathy and Empathy.

Equivalent Level of Experience: 1D6+2

Attacks per Melee: Three attacks per melee by psionic means only; the same number when controlling a host body, dead or not.

Bonuses (in addition to likely attribute bonuses): +2 to dodge as an energy being, +2 save vs magic, +1 save vs psionic attacks, +12 to save vs Horror Factor and is impervious to possession.

Damage: By psionics or physically through its host body.

Magic: None.

Psionics: Needs a 12 or higher to save vs psionic attack. Base I.S.P. is only 20 points, but the Blood Syphon can draw on the P.P.E. of living beings it possesses by draining them of their blood. Conversion is one P.P.E. point gives four I.S.P. points.

Special: Stealing Blood Energy: As soon as the Blood Syphon has possessed a living being, it can drain it of P.P.E. It can absorb up to 5 I.S.P. per drain attack. Each attack is treated as a psionic attack and the victim has a save vs psionic attack. A successful save means that the drain attack failed. As long as the Blood Syphon has a physical body – no matter whether the host is still alive or already a Mock Zombie – the creature must physically drink the blood with its host to be able to consume the blood of others through Stealing Blood Energy! It has no other means to consume blood for P.P.E.

When the possessed victim is completely drained it will die and become a *Mock Zombie*. Use the rule of *Zombies are always Hungry* (**Dead Reign® RPG**, pages 23-24), especially with respect to the curative and restoring effects of P.P.E. consumption as well as the common human and animal P.P.E. numbers.

Limited Psionic Powers: Bend Metal (3 or 8), Bio-Manipulation (the evil eye; 10; described on page 78 of BtS-I), Empathy (4), Empathic Transmission (6; described on page 87 of BtS-I), Hypnotic Suggestion (6), Levitation (varies), Mind Block (4), Presence Sense (4), See Aura (6), See the Invisible (4), Sixth Sense (2), Telekinesis (varies), Unlimited Telepathy (no I.S.P. cost).

Allies: None per se.

Enemies: None per se.

Habitat: Wherever there is life.

Note: Even though the Mock Zombie's stats, etc., are used for the host body, it is still the Blood Syphon who is in charge, so that you basically have a diabolical and very highly intelligent zombie, or zombie-vampire if you will, as a result.

Justice's Return

A Short Story for Rifts®

By Mark Oberle

The crackling of the small campfire overpowers the night calls of the oversized insects just feet from the small camp. Even the small brook nearby sounds like a mere trickle in comparison to the miniature inferno in front of him, but the man's keen ears do not hear this.

The wood smoke fills the camp with a pleasantly acrid aroma, masking the smell of the leather tanning on racks beside the crudely constructed shelter the man calls home. But his large, peaked nose does not smell this.

Embers leap into a cloudless sky that hold a myriad of twinkling lights and a pale sickle that seems sharp enough to cleave the world in two. Wisps of smoke curl into an array of serpentine shapes, drifting through the cool mountain air. But the man's unblinking hazel eyes do not see this.

The gentle breeze stirs the tops of the evergreens, making them bend and sway as if in some secret ritual dance. The strands of the man's unkempt hair and beard, dark brown with the first hints of gray, are tugged at by the invisible currents, as are the frayed ends of his sackcloth shirt. But the man's motionless form does not feel this.

Marcus Vedran sits and stares intently at the heart of the small but fierce blaze before him, but his mind tarries elsewhere. Just now he focuses on a face. A familiar face, that of a man he knew quite well in his youth, when they were the best of friends. Marcus sees that face stare at him in disbelief, then contort with pain as he looks down at his own side. As Marcus follows the man's gaze, he sees his hand grasping at the sword that pierces the man's heart, having been thrust through the ribs just below his left armpit... just between the two plates of ancient-style armor protecting the vulnerable area.

A sound from the present finally manages to find its way into Marcus' mind, snapping him out of his trance. Hoof beats in the distance, slowly coming up the mountainside toward his camp. A dour look spreads across his face as he reaches for his hunting rifle... he's not expecting visitors.

* * *

The saddle-weary rider comes to a halt within sight of the fire-lit camp, with a large riding cloak hanging loosely off of their bulky form and billowing in the breeze. The figure leans forward and the exhausted horse plods the remaining distance into the ring of light. As soon as it nears the fire, a gravelly voice calls out from the darkness.

"Hold right there mister! I don't recall invitin' you to my fireside, so I'd drop any weapons I was carryin' if I was you, least if ya wanna keep your brains in that skull a' yourn."

The rider's short arms slowly release the reins and reach skyward.

A meek and raspy voice replies, "I'm unarmed sir. Iffin you'll let me drop my hood you'll see I mean no harm."

"Make a move other n' that an' you'll be the one droppin'," comes the answer from a different direction than before.

The hood slides slowly down guided by one of the rider's small hands, only to reveal the frightened and dust-covered face of a young teenage girl. Her golden-brown curls have been gnarled by the winds and there are streaks of dried mud across her cheeks where her tears made the dust into crude war-paint. A sleeping young boy, all of two years of age, sits slumped forward into a rolled saddle blanket between him and the saddle horn.

"Serena? What in the seven hells you doin' out this far at night, girlie?!" Marcus asks as he steps into the light with his rifle lowered. "With that youngin' no less!"

"Lookin' fer you Mister Vedran," she says with a faltering voice and wincing expression. "Yer the only one that kin help."

* * *

The flickering light plays across the two expressions sitting across the fire from one another, one of exhaustion and concern, the other a brooding scowl. Taking a careful sip of steaming tea, the young lady speaks, "They rode into town just after dawn..."

Serena stands at the center of a small plaza, drawing water from the town well for her morning chores. To the north, just visible past the tattered canopy of her family's stucco-fronted café and bar, a trail of dust rises skyward. She hurriedly pours the water into the jug at her feet and runs with it as best she can into the dimly lit bar, pausing on the front step long enough to make out the three hovercycles and single jeep speeding toward the town.

The ragtag group of vehicles speeds past the family's humble establishment, through the town square, and pulls to an abrupt stop in front of the clinic that serves both human and animal patients in the tiny community. The hard-looking hovercycle riders jump off their high-tech mounts and draw menacing weaponry. Decked out in heavily battered, filthy, patchwork armor that matches the battle-scarred condition of their vehicles, there is no doubt that these men are bandits.

While the three hovercycle bandits force their way into the clinic, the driver of the jeep along with his passenger, a burly Headhunter with two obviously bionic arms, recover a wounded comrade from the bed of the dust-covered vehicle and help him through the now-open door. Inside, they lift the injured bandit, bleeding from a severe abdominal wound, onto an exam table as two of the hovercycle bandits drag the town's doctor and his wife into the room still in their bedclothes. The Headhunter, leader of the small gang, draws his Big Bore Revolver and motions for Doc Nelson to get to work.

By midday, despite the glaring sun and the presence of a bandit manning the machine-gun mount on the jeep, a group of about twenty townsfolk has gathered in a rough semi-circle around the clinic. An angry roar emanates from within the clinic, followed by the blood-soaked doctor flying eight to ten feet out the front door. A collective gasp ripples through the crowd, but the machine-gunner keeps them at bay by working the slide of the weapon with an audible *KA-CHAK*.

The Headhunter appears at the door, snarling with rage and carrying his huge pistol. He stalks down the steps to where Dr. Nelson is picking himself up from the dust and delivers a powerful kick to the man's ribs, sending him sprawling once more. The bandit leader reaches down and grabs the coughing doctor by his collar and delivers a brutal pistol-whip to the side of his head. But as he steps back and takes aim at the now-unconscious doc, Father Reyes, the town priest, rushes forward and seizes the bandit's metal arm, imploring him to spare Doc Nelson's life. Surprised and further enraged, the Headhunter flings the old priest to the ground with one arm and fires a single shot into his chest. As many of the townspeople stand aghast and the rest flee, the murderer motions for his men to bring Doc Nelson along and turns north.

Meanwhile, Serena's mother, Mariana, a weatherworn but ruggedly beautiful barmaid with long, dark hair and even darker eyes, observes the tragedy from the doorway of their bar. At the sound of the gunshot, she makes haste into the building and up the stairs to the family living quarters. In her bedroom, she flips open a worn steamer trunk and produces a large blanket and canteen. After retrieving a small coin purse from the nightstand, she half-runs down the hall to her young son's room to find Serena helping him put his boots on.

"Here," Serena's mother starts as she hands the items to her, "take these and put 'em in the saddlebags." She then pulls one side of her dress up and removes a small ankle-holster containing a Wilk's derringer. "And ya know what to do with this should you need it." Ignoring the look of concern on her daughter's face, Mariana continues, "Take yer brother out the back and hide in the wagon. If I 'ent come an got ya by dark then you saddle up that ol' mare and ride out to Vedran's camp at Red Brook." Grabbing Serena firmly by the shoulders and staring intently into her eyes, she adds, "Ya don't come back in here 'til I come get ya, no matter what happens, hear me?"

"Yes ma'am."

At the back door, the family pauses long enough for Serena's mother to kiss them both on the cheek before shutting the door behind the children and returning to the bar. Serena and her brother slip underneath the faded blue tarp stretched over the single-horse wagon, which sits behind the small horse stall at the back of the yard.

By dusk, the sounds of the rowdy marauders, hoots, hollers, and breaking glass, can be heard from within the bar. Serena slips out of hiding, saddles the family's horse, positions her frightened brother in the saddle, and rides out of town as fast as possible. Galloping west, she utters a silent prayer that she can find her way in the dark.

"Yer the only one within a hundred miles a'here that can do sumthin' about them bushwhackers. Jimmy Dawes says you're a knight!" For a moment her face brightens. "Sir Vedran the Just they call ya," Serena shoots the surly hermit a pleading look across the fire.

Marcus does his best to pull the cuffs of his sleeves down and cover his cyber-armor as his frown deepens to a seemingly impossible depth. "I'm no knight, I'm no kinda hero, and I'm 'fraid I can't do much for ya," he says matter-of-factly. "I ain't taken up a sword in years now, an' I don't aim to neither. Y'all can stay here the night, but come morning, I'll take you two back to town and that's all. With any luck, them scalawags will have moved on down Pecos-way by then."

Confusion contorts Serena's face as she listens to Marcus' unexpected answer. Her rebuttal comes fast and furious, "But what about my mother? What about Doc Nelson? If you don't do nuthin' there might not be a town to go back to!"

"Yer not listnin' to me, girlie, I gave up fightin' before I even came out here. That ain't who I am anymore," Vedran attempts to explain. His eyes drift down to his calloused hands as he speaks, trying to avoid the desperation and hurt in the young lady's eyes.

"But... but... I thought you was someone that did the right thing," Serena starts shaking her head as tears well up in her eyes once more, "a good guy, Padre Reyes was yer friend 'cause o' that. He even gave you his bible; I saw it there in yer tent!" she exclaims, pointing an accusing finger at a thick black book lying on top of a pile of clothing to one side of her sleeping brother.

Marcus lets her rage at him unhindered. Nothing Serena could say could make him any more ashamed of himself than he already is. Her voice fades away as Vedran finds himself reliving the past once more. He and his friend argue face to face, furious at one another. His friend strikes him to the ground with a fierce left hook and starts to walk away. Sir Vedran lunges to stop him... the sword... the look of betrayal.

Serena stares at him with a mix of disappointment and sadness. "Padre Reyes died tryin ta protect people. Seems to me a friend that owed him as much as you do would wanna see that through," the young lady practically spits. "But since you won't do nuthin' I guess I gotta figure sumthin' out myself." She stands with a look of determination etched upon her young face and storms to the saddle lying beside the tent. After fishing around in the saddlebag for a moment, she produces the laser derringer and checks its charge.

Marcus sits in stunned silence for a moment before speaking in a strong and even tone. "Hold it right there, missy. Before you go tryin' to get yerself killed, do you even know The Rites?"

"What does *that* matter?" Serena asks bitterly, her back to the reticent former knight.

"Because if you're gonna be buryin' people ya ought to know the words that need said over 'em. If you don't know The Rites, then it's best you let me handle it."

Serena turns to find him standing close behind, shoulders straight and the frown replaced by a frank stare. She cracks a little smile of hope infused with a bit of pride, for her words have found their mark. "I'll saddle her up for ya then."

"Naw, that tired piece of horseflesh ain't gonna get me there quick enough."

"Well then, where's your horse?"

"Buried him over a year ago."

"Then how you gonna-" Serena begins to ask.

"I said I buried him," Vedran interrupts while walking to the edge of his camp. He whistles three sharp tones and stands watching a patch of ground roughly ten feet away. In a few seconds, the ground shifts and roils before releasing the form of a jet-black Arabian stallion decked out in ornate combat barding and saddle with two large saddlebags at its sides. Small patches of the hide have been damaged or worn away, revealing the dull gray metal beneath. Without even turning around to view the shocked expression on Serena's face, Marcus steps forward to clear away the remaining dirt on the saddle and smirks. "I never said he was dead."

* * *

Sir Vedran gallops his robotic mount at breakneck speed down the mountainside, savoring the cool night air as it rushes by. He begins remembering what it was like to be truly alive as his mind starts to climb out of the abyssal depression that has consumed him for too long. Once he reaches the creek in the valley below, he engages the built-in thrusters and splashes into one of the deeper pools, disappearing below the surface. He and the horse emerge on the other bank, soaking wet but much cleaner.

In a small clearing, he replaces his wilderness garb with the heavy plate armor from the waterproof saddlebags. As he goes through the ritual of donning the suit he hasn't worn since going into seclusion, now slightly rusted from neglect, he finds his mind drifting back to the memory of the confrontation with his friend three years ago. He sees himself and his fellow knight standing eye to eye, screaming at one another, sneering and snarling in anger as they gesture toward a figure tied to a tree behind Sir Vedran. A young, dark-skinned, bald man in black armor that slumps, unconscious and with a bleeding head wound, against his bindings... that is what the comrades argue about. Marcus is stricken down. His friend stalks toward the unconscious man with a Vibro-Saber in hand. Sir Vedran lunges to stop him and unintentionally runs him through with his Psi-Sword...

The grizzled Cyber-Knight shakes his head in an attempt to clear his mind. He can't let himself think of that now, not when innocent lives may hang in the balance. He owes it to the two people that have set him back on the path he devoted his life to. He climbs into the saddle and spurs his horse towards town.

* * *

The oil lamps cast a warm glow on the walls of the cantina, decked out in pre-Cataclysm memorabilia like the large Texas state flag and an oil painting of the Alamo. The atmosphere would be warm, inviting, and even friendly if it weren't for the current "patrons." Doc Nelson is slumped in the corner under the painted stump that is hung as a dartboard. Battered and bloody, he sits in a ring of broken bottles while a couple of the bandits throw knives at the stump and their empties at him. Two scared young ladies huddle together, both sobbing, at a table nearby with Mrs. Nelson trying to keep them calm.

Mariana tends the bar with a black eye, split lip, and her dress hanging off her shoulder on one side where it has been torn. One of the hovercycle bandits makes an attempt at dancing with an unwilling local girl while a frightened middle-aged man dressed in farm clothes nervously plays the small piano in the corner. The Headhunter sits at a table near the bar, drinking rot-gut whiskey straight from the bottle and smoking a pungent cigar. His dead comrade slumps in a chair across from him with a full shot glass in front of him.

From outside, there comes the sound of raised voices, "Bar's closed, old-timer." A moment later, the sound of grunts and vocalizations of pain before a body comes flying through the blanket hung over the front entrance, tearing it down as the unconscious form of another hovercycle bandit lands on the floor of the bar. Sir Vedran, in a royal blue riding cloak that conceals his armor, steps in over the thug without so much as a downward glance. "You got five minutes to get the hell outta town," he says while glaring at the bandits standing around the room. The knight nods his head back toward the unconscious bandit behind him, "and take yer trash with you."

The music dwindles to a stop. Whether it is the copious amount of alcohol running through their bloodstreams or the sheer audacity of the cloaked intruder, the bandits look to one another, unblinking, for some clue as to what they should do about the threat. The bandit leader looks up from drowning his sorrows at the figure that dares to disturb their impromptu wake. Dismissing him as a headstrong woodsman with more guts than brains, the Headhunter smirks as he signals the three remaining bandits to deal with him. Cautiously, the three thugs stalk towards Sir Vedran until they stand directly in front of him as well as to either side. Marcus Vedran simply stands and waits.

The previously dancing bandit, now to the right of Marcus, is the first to make a move. Unarmed, he attempts to grab Sir Vedran's right shoulder and hold him in place for the other two to assail him. Marcus lets him do so only to retaliate by shrugging off the riding cloak in the man's hands and lashing out with a swift elbow to the throat, sending the attacker stumbling backward, gasping for breath. The sight of the ancient-style plate armor Marcus wears changes the demeanor of the remaining two assailants. This man is a more serious threat than they had thought.

One of the bottle-throwers is next to act, swinging an empty whiskey bottle he has retrieved from a nearby table in an overhand arc at the left side of Sir Vedran's unarmored head. The Cyber-Knight intercepts the bottle with his forearm, causing it to explode into a shower of glass shards. The third bandit takes the moment to draw a combat knife from a boot sheath, holding the razor-sharp weapon in a reverse grip that indicates the man knows quite well how to use it.

Now it is Marcus' turn to go on the offensive, seizing the bottle-wielding bandit by his right arm and executing a shoulder throw that dislocates the attacker's shoulder and sends him flying into his still-gasping cohort. They both land in a heap just in front of the piano and don't immediately rise. Seeing an opening, the third bandit rushes forward and swings his deadly steel in a sideways arc at Sir Vedran's carotid artery. But, the Cyber-Knight is quick enough on his feet to just avoid the slash and strike out with his right leg at the attacker's ankles, sending the would-be killer sprawling near the unconscious form of the door guard.

Upon seeing his men so easily dealt with, the Headhunter has had enough. Growling through gritted teeth, he stands quickly to face the old Cyber-Knight. While his left arm throws the table aside with ease, the right draws his deadly Big Bore from its holster. But, the mechanical limbs that have served the Headhunter so well in the past betray his intent to Sir Vedran's Zen abilities. Before the bandit leader can level a shot, Marcus uses his powers of telekinesis to fling a chair into the man's gun hand, knocking the pistol from his grip.

Though his pistol is flung across the room, the Headhunter is far from disarmed, and the defiant sneer on his face shows his confidence. With a menacing *SCHIK*, a retractable Vibro-Saber slides out of his right forearm and hums with a malice not typically expressed by machinery.

Sir Vedran is unfazed by the attempt to rattle him, and responds by holding his right fist straight out in front of him while fixing the bandit leader with a stolid gaze. Blue-white tendrils of energy wind their way around the Cyber-Knight's gauntlet before shooting out to the left in a dazzling flash to form the blazing, translucent image of a dual-edged broadsword. Sir Vedran the Just has once again taken up his sword… and bathed in the blue-white light of the weapon, the bandit leader seems decidedly less confident.

With a bloodlust roar, the Headhunter closes the distance and swings his blade in an arc that would cleave an unarmored opponent from kidney to clavicle. But once again, Vedran's supernatural combat senses prevail as he spins to his left, avoiding the brutal slice and answering with a diagonal slash at the back of the man's knee. Marcus is rewarded by a shower of sparks as the Psi-Sword cuts into the servo that drives the bionic joint. A shower of sparks illuminates the thin haze of tobacco smoke. But instead of felling the Headhunter as Marcus expects it to, his opponent keeps his feet and lashes out with the saber in a quick reverse strike. The high-frequency weapon gouges a jagged line into the knight's thick shoulder pauldron before he has a chance to take a step back.

Seizing the opportunity afforded by staggering Sir Vedran, the hobbled Headhunter pivots on his locked right leg and moves to press the attack. Drawing back his right arm, the bandit leader steps toward Marcus and lunges as hard as he can, intent on driving his deadly Vibro-Saber straight through the knight's breastplate. Sensing the piston-like stab coming, Vedran throws his left forearm in the path of the blow and summons a kite-shaped sheet of force that matches the appearance of his Psi-Sword. The ultrasonic blade skitters across the surface of Marcus's Psi-Shield but the force of the Headhunter's strike causes the middle-aged knight to stumble further backward toward the bar.

Limping forward to press the attack, the murderous near-cyborg raises his right arm over his head. Sir Vedran counterthrusts as he regains his footing, attempting to seize the opening. But the Headhunter is no green rookie. He ducks his head to the right and grasps Marcus' sword arm. As the man brings his Vibro-Blade down to hew the trapped limb, Sir Vedran looses a furious roar and slams the Psi-Shield forward with all his might. Blood from the bandit leader's split lip and busted nose creates a small spray up the translucent barrier. A lesser warrior would have been knocked unconscious but the Headhunter is only driven a step back and loses his grip on his opponent. Marcus gives him no chance to recover.

Swinging the Psi-Sword in a diagonal underhand arc, he clips the bionic left hand being raised in a defensive posture. The potent psychic weapon removes the thumb and index finger along with a portion of the hand and carves a shallow, red line in the unarmored chest of the knight's foe. Following it up with a right-legged, snap side-kick to the bandit leader's fresh wound, Sir Vedran is rewarded by the crunch of a couple ribs beneath his boot and the bandit leader landing heavily on his back.

Despite the pain of his broken ribs, the Headhunter attempts to push himself to a sitting position, but a flashing blue blade strikes home and separates his supporting right arm at the elbow. Severed from its power source, the thrumming Vibro-Blade falls silent. The man falls back to the floor, growling and snarling. Before he can move again, Sir Vedran's armored boot steps firmly onto his opponent's sternum as he positions the point of his Psi-Sword just millimeters from the Headhunter's Adam's apple.

"Yield."

"Screw you," the pinned killer spits, blood spraying from his lips. "I know yer kind won't kill in cold blood... knight. And you don't look like no vengeance-takin' type."

Leaning closer and toeing the Headhunter's broken ribs, Vedran responds through clenched teeth, "Guess no one ever told you that we're the law in places like this, huh? And seein' as how Padre Reyes was the judge the few times that role needed fillin', guess that makes me lawman, judge, *and* executioner now." Understanding crosses the bandit leader's face, but he just scowls in return and averts his eyes. Straightening back to a standing posture, Marcus adds, "So you pile of Grigleaper crap, you have the right to remain silent." Lifting his foot several inches off the Headhunter's chest as he finishes this ancient lawman's coda, Sir Vedran brings it viciously down on his quarry's face.

* * *

Memories flash one after another like scenes from a poorly spliced movie. The once sturdy walls of Tolkeen crumbling, the city burning, refugees pour through one of the gaps as Sir Vedran and his fellow knights fend off monsters and CS soldiers alike. Now the knights, fewer in number and many of the remaining wounded, lead a ragged band across the northern wilds. Now a squad of CS soldiers lays in ambush for the fleeing survivors. Now the few standing knights charge up a slope to engage the soldiers as scattering civilians are cut down while they run for cover. A single troop stands behind his squad screaming at them to hold their fire. And finally, the argument replays, Marcus lunges forward, and he is left standing over his fallen friend with blood on his hands.

* * *

The sun is setting on the day after the barroom showdown, and two figures stand on a hill overlooking the town. Both wear new CS medium armor, though only one wears her helmet. She has the rank insignia of a 1st Lieutenant, and addresses her Captain who is surveying the town with digital binoculars and holding his helmet under one arm.

Through the viewfinder the Captain can see four of the fugitives he's been chasing shuffling slowly towards his position atop the hill. They have been stripped of everything but clothing and all seem to be injured. Sweeping his view over to the dusty little town behind the fugitives, the figure of a man swinging from the end of a rope attached to the platform of a makeshift windmill catches his eye. Zooming in, he can confirm it is the head of the gang that attacked the CS communications outpost, though he is missing his right arm.

Wondering how this hard-bitten bunch was chewed up by a no-name frontier town, the Captain slowly pans his binoculars back and forth looking for defenders. After a few moments, movement draws his attention to a hill on the western edge of the settlement. Townsfolk are beginning to drift away from the little graveyard wearing the best outfits they could muster, many are still crying. But it is the figure sitting astride a metal horse that holds the Captain's attention... the figure saying goodbye to a woman and two children... the figure clad in a knight's armor with his shoulders straight and head held high... the figure who's careworn face is smiling a solemn smile as he speaks...

"Sir, do you want us to sweep the town?" There is no response from the Lieutenant's CO... he seems lost in thought, transfixed. At once the young woman's questions seem to come from very far away, "Captain? What is it you see?"

Through the blood and sweat in his eyes, a lone CS captive watches a Cyber-Knight kill his brother in arms in order to save him from retribution. He fights to lift his head, to say something... anything to thank his unlikely savior. He loses this fight and falls unconscious once more.

"Captain?"

The officer snaps back to reality, "No, Lieutenant Reeves, that won't be necessary." He commands in a clear and strong voice. "Send O'Malley and Rico down to secure the prisoners approaching our position."

"They're surrendering?"

"Looks that way."

"The hilltop is silent as the Lieutenant relays orders via her helmet radio. "Sir," she asks after a few moments, "permission to speak freely?"

"Go ahead," the CO answers without taking his binoculars from his eyes.

"You seem spooked, sir. What do you see down there?"

The youngish, dark skinned captain lowers his binoculars to reveal a small, jagged scar just above his right eyebrow. Turning to descend the north face of the hill and head back to the Mark-V APC parked below; the Captain shoots his junior officer an almost wistful smirk.

"Justice."

The Kingdom of New Oslo

Optional Source Material for Rifts®

By David Collins

Size: 19,000+ square miles (49,209 square km), not including the NGR military base just north of the submerged ruins of Oslo.

Population: 2.7 million humans and 2.5 million D-Bees. The nation continues to grow rapidly.

History

Unlike so many of the communities scattered across Rifts Earth, New Oslo is not a remnant of a pre-Rifts nation or built with technology salvaged from the past. It is instead one of the few new kingdoms built from the ground up. In 82 P.A. (A.D. 2368), Ewald von Dierks, a relatively wealthy manufacturer in the New German Republic, decided that human supremacy was not desirable, even if it was arguably necessary to the survival of his nation. He also came to the conclusion that this evil, if not countered soon, would be almost impossible to root out when the Gargoyle Empire was finally destroyed. Thus, he embarked on an ambitious experiment to prove that humans and D-Bees could live together in peace for the betterment of all.

In order to get support for his experiment from the NGR government and Triax (with whom he was a minor competitor), he disguised his work as a matter that would aid and strengthen the beleaguered republic. To the government, he stated his ambition to build a new nation in the relatively safe regions of southern Sweden which would be patterned after his homeland. There he could build new manufacturing complexes that could produce needed robotic parts and materials for the NGR, while at the same time, giving the army a place to remove peaceful D-Bees who illegally remained in the NGR.

The NGR was sympathetic, but did not have the means on hand to simply give von Dierks everything he needed. Instead they provided raw materials for his own manufacturing plants so that he could make the tools and machinery necessity demanded. Moving forward with his plans, Ewald took several years to prepare all that he would need to start his domain. By 87 P.A. (A.D. 2373) he was ready. Moving north with over 100,000 colonists, he established his first settlement, and capital, near the ruins of Vara, not far from Lake Vänern. The site was chosen because the old pre-Rifts city, while destroyed in the cataclysm, was at a central location and provided a large amount of salvageable building materials used to speed up construction of the new city. From there, he has started dozens of settlements and communities extending from Lake Vänern to Lake Vättern and down to the sea, which is now as far inland as the ruins of Borås. Almost without exception, all of the petty kingdoms that once dotted this area were peacefully absorbed into the growing nation.

In conjunction with Ewald's colonization, the NGR military set up a significant military base north of the ruins of Oslo (now underwater), where the new nation could be guarded and experiments in naval warfare conducted (see **Rifts® World Books 7: Rift® Underseas™** for more details). The restricted zone around the base extends as far as the old border between Norway and Sweden. Past that point, few humans and no D-Bees are allowed. Trespassers caught near the border will be turned back. Those that get closer to the base are often shot on sight or captured for questioning by the NGR military patrols in the area.

Under the protection of the NGR military, Ewald von Dierks has built a thriving nation that continues to expand at a rapid rate, with a constant influx of refugees from the continent, colonists from the German cities, and D-Bee deportees from the border regions surrounding the NGR.

Government

New Oslo is technically a monarchy, with Ewald von Dierks the supreme law of the land. However, his power is firmly based in the rule of law and a publicly elected parliament ensures that he does not abuse the power he does possess. Members of Par-liament are elected every two years from districts determined by population. (Because of the massive population growth the kingdom has had over the last 15 years, the districts are simply announced by the government before each election.)

Ewald has already drawn up plans for the day he will step down as the monarch of New Oslo. He plans to turn control over to an elected Prime Minister who will have far more limited powers than he currently possesses while he becomes a figurehead monarch. However, he will not go through with this plan until his nation has stabilized and the influx of refugees tapers off, probably not for at least another five years.

The laws of the nation are rather harsh. This became necessary in order to control the constant influx of people and to keep the crime rate down to a minimum. Minor crimes are generally punished by forced labor in public works (for a period of weeks or months, depending on the seriousness of the crime) or fines. Repeat offenders are either deported (rarely back to the NGR) or can face execution! Despite this rule of iron law, the courts are fair and the level of punishment fits the crime as closely as possible. Ewald is also determined to alter the laws of the kingdom once things settle down. He has no intention of allowing his nation to remain so stringent forever.

Magic and those who use it are not generally tolerated. Peaceful mystics that work for the betterment of the community are rarely molested, but they are also offered free passage to either Tarnow (see **Rifts® Mindwerks™**) or New Camelot

(**Rifts® England**). Necromancers, mages that engage in human sacrifice and those who use their powers to harm or enslave others, are often executed after a very short trial!

Psychics must be registered with the government, but are treated well and are generally considered "gifted" instead of freaks or mutants. They are taught to use their abilities for the good of all and are frequently offered jobs where their powers can best serve the kingdom (psychics with physical and sensitive powers are welcomed into the police forces, etc.). Those whose abuse their powers are captured and imprisoned if possible. Those that kill or enslave others are executed.

D-Bees within New Oslo are treated far better than their counterparts on the continent. They have almost all the legal rights as a human, receive protection under the law, and are paid 40% to 50% the wages a human would get for the same job (as opposed to 25% in Germany). Ewald has been quietly increasing the rights of the non-humans within his domain and hopes to see the day when they have full equality. For the most part, the D-Bee communities in New Oslo realize that they have it better than they would elsewhere and show great loyalty to the new nation.

Society

While recognized as an independent nation, New Oslo is essentially a colony that was started for the good of the New German Republic. It produces raw materials, robotic parts, electronics, and foodstuffs which are shipped in bulk back to the continent. Almost all luxuries must still be imported from the NGR.

In the north, timber and mining are the prime industries. The pre-Rifts cities of Torsby, Charlottenberg and Äppelbo have all been rebuilt as mining towns while Filipstad and Nora both send paper and lumber products south. Each of these communities has a population of about 5000.

Between the lakes and extending south, farming is the main concern of the inhabitants. Dozens of small (population of 2000 or less) towns dot the land, surrounded by the fields and orchards they care for. Livestock are also everywhere, with cattle, sheep and hogs raised for their meat. There is at least one cannery in each major settlement to preserve the food meant for the NGR.

Along the new west coast, the cities of Borås, Alingsås, and Trollhättan all stand strong again as centers of manufacturing, fishing and shipping. (They have populations of nearly 800,000 beings each.) It is from these cities that the goods of Oslo are sent abroad and each has a strong contingent of NGR power armor troopers as well as the local defense forces stationed there.

The capital, built on the site of the ruins of Vara and renamed New Oslo, is a large manufacturing center that is constantly expanding. Currently it has a population of 750,000 humans and 100,000 D-Bees. At the southern edge of Lake Vättern, the last major city of the nation, is the rebuilt Jönköping, with nearly 500,000 humans and 80,000 D-Bees.

As a new nation, Oslo is filled with all of the vigor of a frontier community. Normally, crime and lawlessness are extensive in such a society, but Ewald von Dierks has maintained the iron rule of law to curb the worst of these excesses. Still, control is often hard to maintain in the new settlements because of the explosive population growth. The worst problems seem to be gang related (both human and D-Bee). Though Ewald and the police are willing to tolerate some rowdiness on the part of the local youth, serious infractions are dealt with quickly and severely.

Like its parent nation, New Oslo requires all males over the age of 17 to either enroll in the military for five years or work in the manufacturing complexes for six years at minimum wage. Unlike the NGR, however, farmers in the smaller communities are exempt from these requirements and D-Bees are often trained to serve in the militia, especially in the outlying regions of the country. Refugees and colonists who seek entry into the nation must either demonstrate some valuable skills (technician, soldier, etc.) or be apprenticed for at least five years in some trade, often farming or doing lumber work in the north. No one is allowed not to work. With the growth of the manufacturing centers and the constant expansion of the farmlands into the south and southwest, unemployment is rarely a problem.

Education is not quite as good as in the NGR, but is still quite high. All human children must attend school until the age of 15 and are encouraged to enter a trade school for the two years before they enter the required work/military service. The literacy rate remains about 70% in the cities and 55% in the outlying areas.

There are schools for non-humans, but they are either held in someone's home or are privately built and staffed by enterprising individuals. In all cases, they are not "officially" sanctioned by the government, but are tolerated. Most often, they resemble the old one-room schoolhouses of ancient times and the books used are salvaged or bought second-hand. Literacy among the D-Bees is approximately 30% to 40%. It is understood by the D-Bees who run their schools that while some in the government desires an education be provided for non-humans, no state run schools will be constructed in order to keep the good will of the NGR.

While the vast majority of the population of New Oslo hails from the NGR originally, there is a significant amount of beings from other lands (about 35%). Some come from England, others from the lands of the Pre-Rifts French and Polish Empires, but many have emigrated from Russia! Most of the refugees from the east are peasants and common laborers who are simply seeking to find a quite place to live away from the battles between the Warlords and the demonic hordes of Russia. Many, however, are former followers of the *Warlord Kahzmer* who fled Russia after their leader was killed by Warlord Burgasov (see **Rifts® Warlords of Russia™**, pages 38-40 for details on that conflict).

Foreign Relations

The New German Republic (NGR): Relations with the "mother country" remain very good, and constant streams of goods from the kingdom are sold to the continent. Also, New

Oslo is recognized as a completely independent nation by the government of the NGR, especially as long as it continues to support the beleaguered republic with supplies. As far as the average German is concerned, the nation is dominated by humans and the D-Bees there have much the same status as those who legally remain within the borders of the NGR. The German government, however, is somewhat disturbed by the status D-Bees seem to hold there, but are too busy with their own problems to press the issue, especially since Ewald von Dierks is obviously so loyal to the New German Republic and the relationship with his kingdom is too beneficial to them.

The Coalition States (CS): While the CS is NOT happy about a nation of humans and D-Bees associating so closely with the NGR, they have been mollified by Ewald's and the NGR's convincing tales that the D-Bees are exploited and controlled as a labor force for the good of humanity, just like they are within Germany itself. Ewald, however, is very concerned (and rightly so) that when the Gargoyle and Brodkil Empires are destroyed, that the CS will put pressure on him and the NGR to either exterminate or expel the D-Bees within both New Oslo and the New German Republic. He is working very hard to make certain that when the time comes, his nation will be ready enough and strong enough to resist that pressure and to encourage the NGR to do the same.

In regards to the recent civil war between the Coalition and Free Quebec, New Oslo is keeping a low profile. With the CS state of Chi-Town upset with Germany, he knows it is no time to allow his nation to be noticed in any major fashion. As such, his kingdom trades with neither the original Coalition States nor the newly independent Free Quebec and sends no goods to North America in general. Ewald is watching the new peace in North America with a very wary eye.

Mindwerks: There are no relations with this kingdom of lunatics and monsters. Currently, New Oslo is too far north to have to worry too much about the *Gargoyle Empire* or the *Brodkil Empire*, both influenced by Minwerk's lead, the self-proclaimed Angel of Death, and her protege, the Angel of Vengeance. However, with the Brodkil Empire actively invading parts of Poland and the Sovietski and regularly conducting raids into Russia, the New German Republic and beyond, it is only a matter of time before one of the two Empires try to invade Oslo. It is inevitable, and Oslo is not ready for such a catastrophic event.

New Tarnow, Poland: This small nation has no official ties with New Oslo, but trades extensively with her northern neighbor. Oslo has purchased nearly two dozen Walesa Cargo Ships to move their goods and over twenty Lightning Hydrofoil Gun Ships to escort the larger vessels. In return, New Oslo has sold weapons, E-Clips and robotic parts to their Polish friends. All of this trade is kept fairly quiet so as to enable the NGR government to easily ignore it.

Some plans are underway to co-develop a number of military vehicles, with the weapon systems and sensors provided by New Oslo and the engines and chassis created in Tarnow. These negotiations are being kept secret for the time being to prevent either the Brodkil or the NGR government from finding out. If the Brodkil knew, they would try to sabotage the work or step up their attacks on the Kingdom of Tarnow before the humans are ready. The NGR would probably protest about any cooperation with any foreign power that relied on magic and non-humans as much as Tarnow does and would try to stop the negotiations as well. If, however, the new vehicle designs simply appear in the Kingdom of Tarnow's armed forces, few ministers in the NGR government would bother to look too deeply into the matter.

Poznan and Wroclaw, Poland: While there is friendly trade between New Oslo and Poznan, it is fairly limited in scope. The Poles produce many of the same goods and parts needed by the NGR, so there is very little that each can offer the other. Relations remain very friendly, but there is little sustained contact.

In the aftermath of Wroclaw, many of the people who lived near the now-destroyed city have fled. Overwhelmingly, the humans have taken up residence in the NGR, but the D-Bees have been fleeing in greater numbers to New Oslo. This influx has strained the infrastructure at the border stations, but the residents of the northern nation were not about to turn the refugees away.

New Oslo's main involvement in Poland is using it as a staging area for the spies and adventurers von Dierks sends into the Brodkil Empire to gather intelligence on his enemies, especially after the destruction of Wroclaw.

Russia: There is limited contact and trade with the **Sovietski** and the **Warlords of Russia**, but trade is limited almost exclusively to purchases of Novyet vehicles and Servo-Rig weapons to mount on them for use by Oslo's defense forces. Ewald will not jeopardize his relationship with the NGR by openly trading with the Russians. On the other hand, using third parties in Poland, Ewald has been quietly trading weapons and information to Warlord Burgasov to support his attacks on the Gargoyles and other monsters of St. Peter's Spine (see **Rifts Warlords of Russia™**). To date, no major Gargoyle nests infest the mountains of Sweden and Norway, and Ewald von Dierks wants to make certain it remains that way.

Warlord Burgasov knows that many of the late Warlord Kahzmer's followers fled to New Oslo after the fighting 10 years ago, but he is unconcerned. As long as those refugees do not stir up trouble in his sphere of influence, they are ignored as cowards that fled from a warrior's death. Should they support rebellion among his people (the government of New Oslo works very hard to make certain that they don't), then he will turn on them with a vengeance.

England: Relationships with New Camelot and Bath are surprisingly good and trade is brisk. Visiting knights are welcome in New Oslo, but are expected to be deputized and obey the law of the land. Troublemakers and those who flout the law (i.e. vigilantes) are escorted to the border and not allowed to return. Unfortunately, while active trade still continues with Berwynmoore, formal relations have become very strained in the last few years, mainly due to the bellicose and bitter nature of the ruling family (see **Rifts® England**). King Arr'thuu approves of the work being done in the new kingdom and the sorcerer Mrrlyn is pondering on how to turn the situation to his advantage in the future. However, both have too many things to deal with at home to worry about New Oslo for the moment.

Armed Forces

The military of New Oslo is divided into three main forces. The first, and most common, are the local militias. Each community is required to field a certain number of troops based on its population. They are trained by members of the regular army and their function is day to day protection of the town or village they are based in. A member of the militia often (70%) is the equivalent of a Vagabond or Russian Villager. The remainder are skilled Wilderness Scouts, Headhunter, or Reaver Soldier/Grunt. The equipment of the militia tends toward medium or light body armors and an energy rifle (the most common are TX-30 Ion Pulse Rifles, TX-43 Light Assault Laser Rifles, or WR-17 Wilderness Laser Rifles) which are drawn from a community armory maintained by New Oslo. Those that can afford to do so often acquire other weapons for themselves. Each village has a communications center that allows it to contact the regular army if the situation warrants it.

The troops of the regular army are comprised of either heavy infantry (heavy body armor and at least two energy weapons) or are power armor and robot vehicle pilots. Through a treaty with the NGR, they are allowed to use the Terrain Hopper power armors (the T-21 and T-C20), the X-60 Flanker, the X-500 Forager Battlebot and a limited number of the scaled-down X-10 Predator power armors. Over 100 Sting-Ray power armors have been purchased from New Tarnow as well as several dozen Stinger Turbo Tanks. (The main laser cannon is often replaced with a more powerful weapon. Ewald is currently in negotiations with Triax to acquire the rights to put variants of the Jager robot's interchangeable weapon systems on the tanks!) New Oslo also relies on a large number of the Novyet combat vehicles (see **Rifts Warlords of Russia** beginning on page 144) for defense. The snow-jet sled and heavy M.D.C. snowmobile are favored in the outlying wilderness areas because of their mobility in winter.

The third and final segment of New Oslo's defense forces consist of German military "advisors." Often, they consist of small groups of officers that organize and train the local defense forces. Also, several contingents of troops guard several key areas within the kingdom: notably the coast, the military base in Norway, and the vital mines of Jönköping. It is also well known that NGR soldiers fresh from training are occasionally assigned to New Oslo to gain some field experience with veteran troops before being sent south into the war zones.

Outside of these groups, New Oslo makes extensive use of independent Headhunters, Wilderness Scouts, Huntsman-Trappers, Explorers, and wandering Knights to scout beyond the borders and bring back important information and intelligence. Adventurers of all sorts are also hired to disrupt, spy on, and sabotage the Brodkil and Gargoyle Empires on the continent.

Rift Activity

The New Oslo region is blessed with only one major ley line that runs north-south between the lakes and the east coast of old Sweden. There are a handful of lesser ley lines in the north, but no known nexus points in the immediate area. Few monsters roam the wilderness areas, generally consisting of a handful of Gargoyles or Russian demons that have wandered over from the Spine of Saint Peter at the edge of the Russia. Several packs of werewolves once lived in the forests, but were annihilated by NGR forces before the first settlers arrived. Now only a few remain in the north and east, hungry for revenge.

The worst dangers for the new nation have come from the sea. Naut'Yll raiders and Horune Pirates have been raiding their shores for centuries and wage periodic attacks against Olso shipping and the coastal cities. However, the severity of the raids has dropped dramatically since the NGR Navy has been operating in the Baltic and North Seas (and unknown to them, the New Navy). (See **Rifts® Underseas™** for details). Raids from bands of Gargoyles and Brodkil as well as other monsters and D-Bees also occur, but such attacks are at the claws of rogue bands. They are not an invasion force or even scouts from the Gargoyle or Brodkil Empires. Earth is a dangerous place, so period attacks from pirates, brigands, monsters and demons are ordinary and expected occurrences.

A growing problem in the north is beginning to trouble Ewald and give his army reason for concern. Packs of **werewolves**, but especially **Hell Hounds** led by **Fenry Demon Wolves** and packs of Fenry are growing increasingly bold and dangerous, attacking isolated settlements and travelers with increasing impunity. Moreover, their numbers seem to be growing, and that his what Oslo's leaders concerned. It suggests that something dangerous may be brewing in the mountains. The worst attacks take place during the long northern winters.

The werewolves and demon wolves seem to be at odds with each other, but both represent a serious problem. No one knows where these beasts, especially the Hell Hounds and Fenry are coming from or why they have begun to appear with such frequency and greater numbers in just the last year or two. The king's military advisors believe the demons may have been driven from Russia by the Sovietski and/or Warlords, while the more superstitious claim they come for an ancient, but forgotten portal to Hell in the north. What they don't know is that a new dark power is stirring in the north.

Places of Note

New Oslo

Population Breakdown: 850,000 approximate total population: 750,000 humans and 100,000 D-Bees.

New Oslo is the capital of Ewald von Dierks' new nation. Built on the location of the ruins of Vara in old Sweden, its name was specifically chosen to represent the growth and reclamation of human civilization on the planet. Some of the largest manufacturing complexes are to be found here, and new factories are being planned and built each year. All of the legal items from **Rifts® World Book Five: Triax and the NGR™** are built here for sale both back to Germany and abroad. A military school, staffed by German officers, is located here to train and organize the kingdom's army.

Connected to the palace and governmental complex is a large office facility staffed by NGR officials. They are here to keep an eye on New Oslo and act as ambassadors to the nation. The occasional Coalition officer also passes through, making certain that the informal alliance between the Americas and Europe is not being jeopardized or that Germany isn't going "soft" on D-Bees. As a result, there are fewer D-Bees in the capital than in the outer settlements, and Thrace (a D-Bee advisor to Ewald, see Notable NPCs below) is often away from the capital. To date, the CS is far more concerned with events happening on the continent and has paid little attention to this colony, seeing it as little more than a deportation zone for non-humans.

In appearance the city is neither quaint nor picturesque. As one military advisor reported back to his commander on the continent, "It is perhaps the most brutally pragmatic city I have ever seen. It feels more like an assembly line than a place to live." No space has been allowed to be wasted and the entire layout of the city was planned before even the first structure was built. The rather Spartan decor of the place is slowly changing, however, as the population becomes more settled and comfortable in its new home.

Of special interest to player characters is the governmental surveying office. Wilderness scouts and mercenaries are hired on a regular basis to go into the wilderness regions to the north and northeast. They are expected to survey the land and bring back news of any useable resources or dangerous inhabitants that can be found there. Substantial rewards are promised to anyone who locates Gargoyle *nests* near the kingdom, so that they can be eliminated as quickly as possible.

Jönköping

Population Breakdown: 580,000 approximate total population: 500,000 humans and 80,000 D-Bees.

Jönköping is the main reason that the NGR was willing to support Ewald's plans for an independent kingdom, for it is located very near one of the richest uranium deposits in Europe! The mining and refining of this precious resource is the main industry of the city, although several large factories are also located here. By treaty with Germany, 70% of all uranium produced must be sold *only* to the NGR or Triax! The remainder is used by New Oslo for its own factories, armed forces, and units sold abroad.

To protect the mines and provide escort for the uranium shipments, a large detachment of German troops are stationed here, though anywhere from a third to one-half of them are often gone from the city at any particular time, either escorting shipments to the coast or patrolling the immediate region around the city. They include:

2,000 Infantry soldiers (500 are local troops).

1,000 DV-15 Sentry-Bots
100 DV-40 Hunter/Killer Drones
200 X-535 Jagers
150 X-60 Flankers
150 X-10A Predators
100 X-10 Predators (local forces trained by the NGR).
40 X-622 Bugs
15 X-1000 Dyna-Max
48 X-2500 Dragonwings
4 X-2700 Black Knights
12 XM-270 Mosquito Air Ships
36 XM-300 Terror Mini-Tanks
24 XM-330 Phantom Hover Tanks
20 T-322 Stinger Turbo Tanks (local forces)

Note: The Stinger Tanks have been upgraded with ion cannons for their turret guns (each inflicts 1D4x10 M.D. per shot and has a 3,000 foot/914 m range).

Borås

Population Breakdown: 792,000 approximate total population: 667,000 humans and 125,000 D-Bees. This does not include the transient/visitor population (mostly foreign sailors and merchants as well as incoming settlers and refugees) of 3D6x1000 people at any given time.

Borås is typical of the coastal cites in New Oslo, serving three main functions. The first is that all potential settlers must pass through the Examination Houses before they are allowed to live in New Oslo. In these facilities, they receive a cursory physical examination, an interview to determine their skills and talents, a quiet background check through NGR channels to weed out known criminals, and psychic "observation" conducted by trained psychic sensitives and military Psi-Stalkers to make certain no monsters, mystics or beings of similar nature are unknowingly let into the nation. The potential applicant is then assigned to an apprenticeship (if an uneducated refugee) or to a settlement to live. Those considered undesirable are turned away or imprisoned if they return at a later date. While this system may seem brutal and oppressive, it has been very effective in controlling the crime rate and keeping the kingdom safe. As such, most settlers are more than willing to put up with the hassle.

Secondly, the city is a food production center. From here the fishing fleet sails out into the Baltic Sea and processing plants line the edge of the area, canning and preserving not only fish, but also the produce sent in from the interior farmlands.

Third, and perhaps most important, Borås is a port city. Ships from the NGR, England, Tarnow, and even Russia stop here daily to drop off and pick up cargo. Merchants from every major country in Europe come here to buy, sell and barter everything from smoked salmon to power armors! Every ship that doesn't come from the NGR must pay a tax to dock and unload/load cargo. All goods bought and sold by legal merchants also carry a 5% sales tax. Each ship docking is searched and smuggling is **not** tolerated by the local officials. Any dock-master caught accepting bribes to look the other way is imprisoned, tried, has all of his worldly possession seized, and then are often executed in the name of national security!

Despite a large and well-armed police force, crime is still a problem. Gangs roam the streets at night and there are those who are paid well to smuggle both items and refugees into New Oslo. Fortunately, both the presence of the local forces and the NGR military detachments keeps the situation under control.

There are two businesses in Borås that may prove of great interest to adventurers. The first of these is Underwater Salvage Operations. It is a company specializing in excavating the pre-Rifts cities that now are submerged under the Baltic Sea. Given the attacks by pirates, the Horune, the Naut'Yll and other monsters that prowl the depths, the company is always happy to hire some extra muscle when going out on a job.

The second company is Families Reunited. With the constant influx of refugees and deportees from the continent, families and loved ones are constantly separated. The founders of this private detective agency, Friedrich and Evelyn Preuss, wanted to help anyone seeking to find family. They are always looking for wilderness-savvy adventurers to go dangerous regions surrounding the New German Republic to look for people (human or D-Bee) left behind by those moving to New Oslo.

Note: A number of squatter villages and towns have grown up along the southern coast (now stretching from the ruins of Markaryd to Tingsryd). Most of these settlements are simply D-Bee communities that are looking for a safe place, any place, where they can live in peace. Unfortunately, others are smugglers dens that move items into and out of the country for a price. About 90% of the time, these communities have been infiltrated either by NGR or New Oslo operatives. When he feels the time is right, Ewald will invite the peaceful settlements into his kingdom as legal towns, provided that they adopt New Oslo's laws as their own. However, he plans to completely crush the smuggler sites first.

New Oslo Characters of Note

Ewald von Dierks

King of New Oslo and CEO of Castle Electronics (das Schloss die Elektronik)

"'We stand on the threshold of a new age.'

"I'm sure you've heard the saying. After all, the propaganda offices here, in the Sovietski and New German Republic, and every other civilized country have probably been beating the idea to death for the last thousand three hundred years.

"Well, would you like to know the truth? The fact is they're wrong. Every single second of our lives is the moment we stand on that threshold. Every moment of every day *we* decide

the future. The repercussions of our decisions may not hit us for a year, a decade, or even a millennium, but eventually they will. Too many of us just walk around with our eyes closed, never seeing that *everything* sets the stage for the next moment. We are blind to the power to shape the universe that all of us possess.

"My father taught me to open my eyes. Perhaps it is my job to open yours."

– The opening to a speech by Ewald von Dierks

Ewald von Dierks is perhaps the most perplexing human in Europe. As a patriot to the cause of the New German Republic, he has created his own kingdom whose primary purpose is to support his homeland's war effort. While he supports the expulsion of D-Bees as a necessary matter for the NGR, he loathes human supremacy and will do nothing to support it directly. He is a ruthless manufacturer who will let almost nothing stand in his way, but he respects a worthy opponent and will not act unduly against those who he considers "worthy of their position in life." He will not go even an inch out of his way to give anything to anyone, no matter how desperate their need, but he will go to extraordinary lengths to put people in a position where they can earn what they need and he makes certain that, if it is within his power, no one starves in his domain.

Ewald von Dierks has set his sights firmly on the future and tirelessly works towards his goal to make the future the one of his personal vision. Though strongly pro-human, he also very much believes that humanity cannot stand alone and that the mistreatment of D-Bees will come back to haunt humanity and undermine everything his people might be able to build.

The future of humanity must, therefore, be built in cooperation with the other races that currently share the planet. Ewald recognizes that most D-Bees are themselves refugees, as lost and confused as any human in the chaos that pervades Rifts Earth. One of his favorite sayings is the old pre-Rifts quip, "If we don't hang together, we shall surely hang separately."

Descended from a family known for its patriotism and loyalty, he has successfully parlayed his family fortune and a mere idea into a nation that holds a great deal of power and wealth. He fully intends to keep building on his ideas until Europe is purged of the Gargoyles, Brodkil and demons that infest it. At the same time, in his vision of that future, humans and D-Bees are equals, working toward even greater goals and ideas. He realizes that this is perhaps the most precarious of his goals, and he is working quietly and steadily to shape the future into something better.

As a natural leader, many people find themselves caught up in his vision and plans even before they realize it is happening. Already, his ability to talk people into seeing his point of view is nearly legendary. A joke is making the rounds in the Triax offices that the company agreed to make him king in another country to prevent him from becoming an emperor in Germany!

Real Name: Ewald von Dierks.

Alignment: Principled.

Hit Points: 52

S.D.C.: 17

P.P.E.: 9

Attributes: I.Q. 14, M.E. 15, M.A. 22, P.S. 10, P.P. 11, P.E. 16, P.B. 13, Spd 14.

Experience: 8th level (Rogue) Scholar/Businessman.

Weight: 153 lbs (68.9 kg).

Height: 5 feet, 8 inches (1.73 m).

Sex: Male.

Age: 45

Disposition: Grim and determined, he is a pragmatic optimist who makes certain that he always knows the odds, and then stacks the deck in favor of his goals. He firmly believes that there is no good which cannot be turned to evil and no evil which cannot be turned to good (figuring out how is the only problem).

Appearance: An intense man with a penetrating stare. As a highly animated person, he can rarely sit still for long and seems to overflow with boundless energy. He chooses to remain clean-shaven and somewhat fit for his public appearances.

Natural Abilities: None, though those who have met him often believe that his ability to talk people into doing what he wants borders on the supernatural!

Magic: None.

Psionics: Lore only, despite rumors to the contrary.

Skills: Language: Euro, Dragonese and American at 98%, Brodkill and Gargoyle at 80%, Literacy: Euro 98%, Dragonese and American at 95%, D-Bee Lore 90%, Demon & Monster Lore 90%, Psychic Lore 95%, Land Navigation 64%, Pilot Automobile 84%, Pilot Hovercraft 98%, Basic Radio 90%, Interrogation Techniques 75%, Streetwise 48%, Intelligence 60%, Find Contraband, Weapons and Cybernetics 54%, Military Etiquette 60%, First Aid 90%, Computer Hacking 60%, Computer Operation 98%, Computer Programming 95%, Basic and Advanced Math 98%, Basic Electronics 80%, Basic Mechanics 80%, Writing 90%, Performance 80%, Art 80%, Gambling 55%, General Athletics, Swimming, W.P. Energy Pistol and W.P. Energy Rifle.

Combat: Hand to Hand: Basic: 5 attacks per melee. +3 to parry and dodge, +1 to strike, +2 to damage and +2 to pull/roll with punch, fall or impact. Critical Strike on a natural 19-20, Kick attack and Judo-style throw.

Allies: Ewald can count on the support of Thrace in most matters, though he holds no illusions about a friendship between them. He also has friends in high places in the NGR government, Poland, Tarnow and England. He is unaware of the danger that Mrrlyn represents or the corruption slowly eating away at King Peter in New Tarnow.

Enemies: Topping this list are the Gargoyle and Brodkil Empires. He intends to be instrumental in their destruction and is constantly working against them. The warlords of Russia see his kingdom as a "lap dog" of the NGR and generally hold him in disdain. Though he doesn't know it yet, his most direct enemy is the demon hound Fenrik.

Equipment: With a moment's notice, he can lay his hands on any legal piece of equipment available in Europe. Illegal items may take one or two days through his contacts. Personally, he tries to avoid combat (he knows he is no fighter), but wears a full suit of T-40 Urban "Plain Clothes" Armor (A.R. 19 and 20 M.D.C.) in private situations and a specially crafted suit of armor (120 M.D.C.) when appearing in public.

Money: He has over 4 million credits in his personal accounts, but tends to invest most of his earnings back into either his business or the kingdom. He has access to over 2 billion credits in cash and 5 billion in equipment through the kingdom!

Thrace Kylrrn

"Advisor" to the King in Matters of Resource Allocation and D-Bee Affairs

"I do not know which scars my soul more. The knowledge of how poorly the other peoples have been treated by the humans and are left to die in the wildlands while the humans protect their own; or that were our positions reversed, and our nation was the realm under siege by the darkness, that we would have done exactly the same thing.

"Now, I have been given the chance to undo what has been done. I will not squander it. And I will not let you squander this chance either."

Thrace is a D-Bee who originates from a far corner of the New German Republic (NGR). He has suffered at the hands of humans for the greater part of his life. His family was fifth generation descendants of refugees from the Rifts. During the ongoing conflicts between the humans and the Gargoyles, his

mother was killed in the fighting and he and his father fled to the NGR for protection. There, his father was killed for refusing to leave and Thrace was ejected with a motley crew of "undesirables" to the lands bordering old Poland. Abandoned and isolated, they were left to live or die.

For nearly ten years, Thrace acted as the leader and protector of his fellow non-humans, teaching them to defend themselves, find food, organize for mutual protection, and how to acquire needed equipment (illegally or otherwise). They hid from the world and tried, fairly successfully, to remain unnoticed by either the human armed forces or the Gargoyles. However, word of this quiet leader quickly spread throughout the ranks of the D-Bees in the region, who came to respect both his capabilities and his success. It is a testament to his abilities that he was able to bring his people together and, despite all odds, survive and prosper.

During this period, he held no love for the NGR, but did not act against the humans because he felt that would only aid the Gargoyles for whom he held absolute loathing. Also, he was afraid that if he did so, he would merely reveal the presence of his community to both sets of enemies and destroy everything he had built.

All this came to an end when he learned that Ewald von Dierks was building a kingdom of his own. It had become common knowledge that this realm was a place where the NGR could "dump" unwanted D-Bees. Furious, Thrace swore that he would hunt down and kill the human responsible for an even greater humiliation against non-humans than he and his people had already suffered. He packed up all of his belongings, left his associates on the Polish border, and departed for New Oslo, intent on murder.

Upon arriving, however, he quickly fell prey to his own leadership talents and reputation. Too many of the D-Bees entering the kingdom knew of him and looked to Thrace for leadership. On the other hand, the humans, looking for any opportunity to make the movement of so many people through the ports easier, hired him as a liaison with the non-humans. Within a month he was organizing settlements and migrations to various communities and making certain that supplies went where they were supposed to go. While he was not happy with the situation, he could not deny that he was doing as much if not more good for non-humans than he had while in Germany. Also, he was beginning to work his way through the system from within, and this would perhaps give him a chance to strike at his perceived enemy.

During his stay, Thrace fully expected to see nothing but humiliation, slavery and degradation of the D-Bees by the nation of New Oslo. However, day after day, he saw examples of humans actually helping the other races and an increase in the rights and living standards of the non-humans. Morally confused and beginning to doubt his mission, matters were decided for him when he discovered that an unscrupulous human had been diverting equipment for sale to the black market to line his own pockets. Quickly Thrace moved against him, garnering enough evidence to convict the villain and then turning him in to the local authorities. Expecting a difficult battle in court, especially since he was a D-Bee accusing a human, he was amazed when the man he had sworn to kill took an active interest in the matter. Within days, Thrace saw his case move from a local matter to a personal war waged by Ewald von Dierks to root out a source of corruption within his kingdom before it could spread!

It did not take the perceptive D-Bee long to realize the real agenda that von Dierks was pursuing. The evidence he had seen over the course of working two years in the Examination Offices of Boräs was confirmed by the personal actions of the king himself. Faced with the truth, he turned aside from his oath of vengeance and has since worked tirelessly to build an even stronger kingdom than even Ewald suspects he has.

Thrace holds no official position in the government, merely being considered an advisor or lesser minister appointed by the king. However, he holds more influence as an "advisor" than many humans have in positions above him. Most of them do not resent this, simply because they understand that he has no ambitions to rise in power and simply wants what is best for the kingdom and "his" people, but there are those envious of him and who would like to see him discredited or removed. Not even his critics doubt his loyalty to the kingdom, however.

He still has too many scars from his past to ever truly like or trust most humans, but he knows that Ewald is a man of his word. If he ever finds himself in such a position, Thrace will die to protect the dream this honorable human has begun to build.

Real Name: Thrace Kylrrn
Alignment: Unprincipled, but in the face of Ewald's force of personality and dream, it is quickly becoming Principled.
Hit Points: 46
S.D.C.: 48

P.P.E.: 4

I.S.P.: 63

Attributes: I.Q. 15, M.E. 13, M.A. 14, P.S. 16, P.P. 17, P.E. 15, P.B.10, Spd 30.

Note: The Narn-Toor racial attribute scores are the same as a human's (3D6).

Experience: 9th level Headhunter.

Weight: 240 lbs (108 kg).

Height: 6 feet, 6 inches (2 m).

Sex: Male.

Age: 42

Disposition: A born leader and natural organizer, Thrace is able to keep track of a thousand details and a deal with a dozen crises at once. Suspicious and distrusting of most humans, he has forced himself to work around his own prejudices for a greater cause. He has found himself becoming more of a crusader than he ever thought himself capable of being.

Appearance: Not easily mistaken for human, Thrace's people call themselves the Narn-Toor. They are tall, lean beings covered with short, wiry brown fur except for the face and hands. Their pawed feet appear much like a cat's and their face is reminiscent of a badger, though vaguely human. Several dozen of the Narn-Toor now live within New Oslo and only a handful remain on the continent.

Natural Abilities: Can see in dimmer light than a human (needs only one half the amount a human would need), but dislikes bright light.

Magic: Lore only.

Psionics: Total Recall and Empathy. Minor psionic.

Skills: Language: Euro, Dragonese and American, all at 98%, Literacy: Euro 70%, Cook 75%, Fishing 80%, D-Bee Lore 65%, Demon & Monster Lore 65%, Magic Lore 25/15/10%, Basic Mechanics 75%, Land Navigation 78%, Weapon Systems 90%, Read Sensory Equipment 80%, Pilot: Automobile 77%, Hovercraft 95%, Jet Pack 86%, and Tank & APC 78%, Detect Ambush 80%, Detect Concealment 80%, Track 75%, Military Etiquette 80%, Find Contraband, Weapons & Cybernetics 50%, Streetwise 32%, Wilderness Survival 70%, Identify Plants & Fruits 65%, Radio Basic 98% and Scrambler 85%, Running, Wrestling, and General Athletics.

Weapon Proficiencies: Energy Rifle, Energy Pistol, Automatic Rifle, Heavy Energy and Knife, all at 9th level of proficiency.

Combat: Hand to Hand: Expert: 6 attacks per melee, +5 to parry and dodge, +3 to strike, +4 to roll with punch, fall or impact, +2 to pull punch. Kick Attack, Judo-style Body Flip/Throw, Paired Weapons, and Critical Strike on a Natural 18-20.

Allies: While he still will not admit (even to himself) that he likes the man, Thrace can count on the full support of Ewald von Dierks for most of his decisions. While the humans of New Oslo generally respect him, he is considered something of a folk hero to the D-Bees of the kingdom. His reputation extends back into many of the smaller squatter communities around the NGR.

Enemies: Several human supremacist groups have threatened his life while some government officials in Germany feel he wields too much power and think he should be removed. He hates the demon hordes of Europe with a passion and longs for the day when their empires are destroyed. Though he does not know it yet, the demon hound *Fenrik* has become his mortal enemy.

Equipment: As a royal advisor, Thrace has access to any legal equipment the kingdom manufactures. He keeps a suit of Explorer body armor, a pair of TX-22 Precision Laser Pistols, and a WR-17 Wilderness "Double" Rifle from his days on the Polish border. He generally drives a hovercycle when he is about on business. His "working clothes" are a set of T-40 Urban "Plain Clothes" Armor (A.R. 19 and 12 M.D.C.), though he will not don his armor when appearing in public.

Money: He generally has 100,000 credits in his accounts. He could be very wealthy if he chose, but he continually spends money for information (generally from independent adventurers, mercenaries and the like) that can be used to strengthen the kingdom.

Fenrik the Demon Hound

"Let them live and run for a while longer. Terror so sweetens human flesh."

This demonic beast claims to be the offspring of the *Great Fenrir Wolf* of Nordic myth (see **Rifts® Pantheons of the Megaverse®**), and the greatest of the *Fenry Demon Wolves,* which makes him a god! While there is no proof to back up his claim, many of the Fenry do worship this malicious beast as their deity. Other beasts also serve Fenrik, especially the supernatural creatures known as **Hell Hounds**. **Note:** If the G.M. chooses to accept Fenrik's claim as more than an idle boast, it is very likely that he is currently on Rifts Earth looking for a way to free "daddy" from his imprisonment.

Perhaps above all other things, Fenrik hates civilization. The creature believes that all sentient beings should live as animals, specifically as his prey. Technology and magic have given too much power to mere mortals and he would like to see that power stripped away, reducing humanity and all other races back to barbarism. To further that end, the mad god Fenrik does what he can to start wars, encourage blood feuds, and otherwise increase the general level of mayhem in the Megaverse among mortals. He revels in the bloodbath that often accompanies his work, and hopes that his efforts will weaken a civilization enough to topple it. Though he hates technology, Fenrik has been on the receiving end of its power too often to underestimate it. He will not be caught off-guard by technology, but he can be surprised by the ingenuity of humans (ironically, he thinks of them as little more than animals), and constantly fails to take into account their adaptability.

In many ways, he represents the dark and animalistic past humanity has struggled so long to grow out of. In his dark and twisted dreams, Fenrik sees a future when he and his followers will lair in the ruins of the NGR and hunt the pitiful human

bradshaw
2017

survivors through the wreckage of their former grandeur. Such is his madness and evil nature.

It is believed by some that Fenrik has been on Earth since before the time of the Rifts (he greeted the general downfall of human culture and civilization with boundless joy) and that he resents the rising of mankind from the ashes. He remains in Europe, fanning the flames of war and working tirelessly to bring about the second destruction of Germany. As such, he absolutely loathes the building of New Oslo. (The other nations of Europe are either the barbarous cultures of monsters like the Gargoyles, or the remnants of previous nations. New Oslo is the first European civilization that has been begun from scratch to Fenrik's way of thinking.)

He is, before all other things, a wolf, and works with a predator's patience to bring about the fall of humanity once again. When he finally does go to war, it will be as a giant wolf. He will strike at his victims repeatedly, bleeding and weakening them until he moves in for the kill. First, New Oslo must be rent asunder, and then the NGR will be the next to fall. Once that has been accomplished, perhaps the Russians will feel his wrath next (or maybe the Americas, he's not sure). But until that is accomplished, he gathers his strength, gains more followers and worshipers, and bides his time until he is ready. Should he ever be thwarted in his quest, he will never rest until he has had vengeance on those who interfered in his work.

Fenrik the Demon Hound

Real Name: Unknown.
Alignment: Diabolic.
M.D.C.: 5,400
P.P.E.: 750
I.S.P.: 130
Attributes: I.Q. 17, M.E. 15, M.A. 6, P.S. 50, P.P. 22, P.E. 20, P.B. 5, Spd 30 but can run for 1D4 hours at a time at a Speed of 110 (75 mph/120 km) but must rest for an hour afterwards.
Experience: 8th level Earth and Air Warlock.
Weight: 4 tons.
Size: 6 feet (1.8 m) at the shoulder and 15 feet (4.6 m) long.
Sex: Male.
Age: Unknown, possibly thousands of years old, probably older.
Disposition: Brutal and vicious, he enjoys the pain and suffering of others. Fenrik revels in terror and will always seek to break an enemy's spirit before rending their flesh. He generally is in control of his temper, acting with patience and guile, but when his plans are blocked or thwarted, he goes into a towering rage that can only be sated in blood (preferably that of those who annoyed him), acting irrationally until he calms down.
Appearance: Appears as a huge, jet-black wolf with glowing yellow eyes. Blood is constantly dripping from its muzzle, as if it has just killed something (not all that unlikely, actually!).
Natural Abilities: Nightvision 240 feet (73 m; can see in total darkness), keen normal vision, see the invisible, turn invisible at will, track by smell 95%, track by sight 75%, dimensional teleport 63%, bio-regenerate 4D6 M.D. per melee, resistant to fire and cold (magic fire and cold, and M.D. plasma do one-quarter damage), magically understands all languages.
Vulnerabilities: Weapons made of silver, Holy weapons and Rune weapons all inflict double damage (if the weapon is an S.D.C. weapon, it will inflict M.D.). Weapons made from the wood of a Millennium Tree and all attacks and defenses of these sentient plants inflict ten times damage! (It is for this reason that he has stayed clear of England so far.)
Magic: All Earth and Air Warlock spells from levels 1 to 5.
Psionics: Has all physical and sensitive powers as well as the super psionic abilities of Bio-Manipulation, Electrokinesis, and Empathic Transmission. All psychic powers are at 5th level of proficiency.
Skills: Humanoid skills mean very little to him, but he has the following abilities that are the rough equivalent of human learning: Detect Ambush 85%, Detect Concealment 75%, Intelligence 90%, Imitate Voices and Impersonation 60%, Interrogation Techniques 70%, Wilderness Survival 98%, Holistic Medicine 75%, Prowl 85%, D-Bee Lore 70%, Demon and Monster Lore 98%, Faerie Lore 85%, Magic Lore 80%, Identify Plants & Fruits 90%, and Trap/Mine Detection 60%. Fenrik is illiterate!
Combat: 8 physical attacks/actions per melee or two by magic.
Damage: Claw 1D6x10 M.D., Bite 2D4x10 M.D., and Pounce 1D4x10 M.D. plus a 20% chance of pinning a human-sized target or smaller but requires two attacks.
Bonuses: +8 to strike and dodge, +6 to parry, +5 on initiative, +6 to roll with impact, but cannot and will not pull punches; +6 to save versus magic and poison/toxin, +3 to save vs and psionics.
Allies: His closest allies include those *Fenry* that worship him and the *Hell Hounds*. He has brought thousands of Hell Hounds with him to Northern Europe and Scandinavia. Should he be destroyed or driven from Rifts Earth, nearly two-thirds of them will vanish into other dimensions. He also counts a number of demons as his followers, including a number of Russian demons (especially *Demon Claws, Il'ya, Stone Demons,* and *Serpent Hounds*). Many werewolf clans of Scandinavia are beginning to accept and worship Fenrik, and he is working to gain the worship of all werewolves on the continent. He has considered an alliance with *Bres the Beautiful*, but doesn't trust the god (the reverse is also true; Bres will never turn his back on Fenrik). *World Slayer Demons* (see the **Rifts® Chaos Earth®** sourcebook: **Creatures of Chaos** for details of these horrid beings) also see Fenrik as a kindred spirit. While they certainly would never trust one another, they have worked together in the past, trying to tear down order and civilization.
Enemies: Generally, humanoids and all beings of good. Since he would like to sow the seeds of discord into the kingdom of New Oslo, he has come to hate Ewald von Dierks and especially Thrace for doing much to keep the D-Bees and humans at peace with each other. Also, he despises the Gargoyle Empire since Gargoyles are meant to be "mere"

sub-demons and definitely not masters of their own destiny. He will, however, not bother the Gargoyles until after the NGR is dealt with. He also desperately hates the Millennium Trees and all who revere those sentient plants. He will support anyone who attacks or kills them.

Most deities do not know about this monster, but those that do generally hate him. He has had several run-ins with various pantheons, but he prefers to keep his distance even from the other evil gods. His worshippers are generally monsters, not humanoids, so Fenrik vies with few deities for followers.

Equipment: Fenrik has no use for human tools except to use them as bait.

Money: He has no wealth and desires none. All loot from his raids is simply left to lie where it is or is given to his followers who cherish such things.

Vehicles and Equipment

New Oslo, and specifically Castle Electronics, produces a number of items, many of which can be found in **Rifts® Triax and the NGR™**. For instance, the corporation is one of the manufacturers that produce the WR series weapons and they also produce all of the legal styles of body armor found in that book. However, Castle Electronics also have produce a line of vehicles used extensively by the NGR military and various civilian companies, including Triax, for the movement of goods and materials. The most common items are outlined below.

CE-135 Light Hover Truck

This light hover truck is designed for moving small loads, 10 tons or less, quickly from place to place. Thousands can be found in use throughout the NGR and New Oslo as delivery trucks, hauling an amazing variety of goods. It is a lightly armored vehicle and is not meant for use in combat situations.

Model Type: CE-135

Class: Civilian Hover Cargo Transport.

Crew: One. An additional passenger can easily be accommodated.

M.D.C. by Location:
* Hover Jets (4) – 40 each
* High-Impact Windshield – 30
* Headlights (4) – 10 each
Cargo Area (open) – 150
Detachable Roof for Cargo Bay – 75
** Forward Cabin/Main Body – 100

* Items marked with a single asterisk are small targets and difficult to hit. An attacker must make a called shot to hit, and even then he is at -3 to strike.

** Depleting the M.D.C. of the main body will destroy the vehicle, making it useless. However, the cargo bay will likely remain intact and the cargo can often be salvaged.

Speed:

Land: Maximum of 150 mph (240 km) when empty. A full cargo will reduce its maximum speed by half.

Water: 20 mph (32 km) when empty, 5 mph (8 km) when fully loaded.

Air: While the truck can hover 2 to 10 feet (0.6 to 3 m) off the ground, true flight is not possible.

Statistical Data:

Height: 10 feet (3 m).

Width: 5 feet (1.5 m).

Length: 14 feet (4.2 m).

Weight: 2 tons empty.

Cargo: The cargo area can store 10 tons of material.

Power System: 80% of the CE-135's are electric (800 mile/1280 km range), 15% have gasoline engines (500 mile/800 km range), and the remaining 5% have nuclear engines with a 5 year life.

Market Cost: Electric: 25,000 credits; Gasoline: 23,000 credits; and Nuclear: 2 million credits. Excellent availability.

Weapon Systems: None.

CE-150 Heavy Hover Truck

The heavier version of the CE-135, this hover vehicle is used most often to haul large cargoes of up to 100 tons from place to place; loggers use it to move trees, miners to move ore, and a host of other possible functions. This rumbling vehicle is a common sight throughout New Oslo, the NGR, and Tarnow. Like the light hover truck, the CE-150 is not meant for use as a military vehicle, but some crews have converted it to such use.

Model Type: CE-150
Class: Civilian Hover Cargo Transport.
Crew: One, but can fit 2 passengers easily into the cab.
M.D.C. by Location:
   * Hover Jets (6; large) – 70 each
   * Directional Jets (8; small) – 20 each
   High-Impact Windshield – 50
   * Headlights (4) – 10 each
   Cargo Bay (enclosed) – 250
   ** Forward Cabin/Main Body – 200

   * Items marked with a single asterisk are small and/or difficult to strike. An attacker must make a called shot to hit and even then he is -3 to strike.
   ** Depleting the M.D.C. of the main body will destroy the vehicle, making it useless. However, the cargo bay will likely remain intact and the cargo can often be salvaged.

Speed:
Land: 140 mph (224 km) maximum when empty, but 80 mph (128 km) maximum when fully loaded.
Water: 50 mph (80 km) when empty, but a mere 10 mph (16 km) when fully loaded.
Air: While the vehicle can hover 2 to 10 feet (0.6 to 3 m) off the ground, true flight is impossible.

Statistical Data:
Height: 15 feet (4.6 m).
Width: 10 feet (3 m).
Length: 25 feet (7.6 m).
Weight: 8 tons when empty.
Cargo: The cargo bay can hold 100 tons of goods.
Power System: Electric (500 mile/800 km range) or Nuclear (5 year life span).
Market Cost: Electric: 80,000 credits; Nuclear: 3 million credits. Excellent availability.

Weapon Systems: None standard, but see the modified CE-155 below.

CE-155 Converted Hover Truck

Certain corporations and small kingdoms have purchased a modified version of the CE-150 in order to haul their goods across dangerous territory. A few have also been purchased by high-tech bandits. More heavily armored than the normal civilian version, the CE-155 possesses a number of weapon systems and has gunner positions for two light or medium power armors.

One of the advantages to the CE-155 is that the weapon turrets can be placed on automatic by the pilot, allowing him greater control in steering the vehicle. The computer will automatically track and fire on the last target that attacked the hover truck, unless directed by a verbal command from either the pilot or copilot. If no targets have fired upon the vehicle, the computer will place the weapons on "stand-by" until an attack occurs.

Model Type: CE-155
Class: Military Hover Cargo Transport.

Crew: One plus can accommodate a copilot and two gunners in light or medium power armor.

M.D.C. by Location:

* Hover Jets (6; large) – 100 each
* Directional Jets (8; small) – 20 each

High-Impact Windshield – 80

* Headlights (4) – 10 each

Cargo Bay (enclosed) – 480

Top Forward Weapon Turrets (2) – 100 each

* Bottom Weapon Turrets (2; forward and rear) – 80 each

Forward Gunner Compartment – 130

Rear gunner Compartment – 100

** Forward Cabin/Main Body – 300

  * Items marked with a single asterisk are small and/or difficult to strike. An attacker must make a called shot to hit and even then he is -3 to strike.

  ** Depleting the M.D.C. of the main body will destroy the vehicle, making it useless. However, the cargo bay will likely remain intact and the cargo can often be salvaged.

Speed:

Land: 140 mph (224 km) maximum when empty, but 80 mph (128 km) maximum when fully loaded.

Water: 50 mph (80 km) when empty, but a mere 10 mph (16 km) when fully loaded.

Air: While the vehicle can hover 2 to 10 feet (0.6 to 3 m) off the ground, true flight is impossible.

Range: Effectively unlimited.

Statistical Data:

Height: 15 feet (4.6 m).

Width: 10 feet (3 m).

Length: 25 feet (7.6 m).

Weight: 10 tons when empty.

Cargo: The cargo bay can hold 100 tons of goods.

Power System: Nuclear (5 year life span).

Market Cost: 5 million credits; excellent availability.

Weapon Systems:

1. **Single Barrel Laser Turrets (2):** On either side of the main cab area, there are two laser turrets. Each covers an arc of 180 degrees on either side of the vehicle and can be raised or lowered 90 degrees. They are not designed to be fired at the same target, but can do so if it is directly in front of or behind the CE-155 and is more than 15 feet (4.6 m) wide. These weapons are typically controlled by the pilot.

Primary Purpose: Defense.

Secondary Purpose: Anti-Missile.

Mega-Damage: 4D6 M.D. per single blast or 8D6 per simultaneous blast from both turrets firing at the same target.

Rate of Fire: Equal to the gunner's attacks/actions per melee round (typically 3 to 6), or 4 attacks per melee when automatically run by the on-board computer.

Maximum Effective Range: 2,000 feet (610 m).

Payload: Effectively unlimited.

Bonuses to Strike: +3 when controlled by the on-board computer.

2. **Lower Single Barrel Laser Turrets (2; one forward, one rear):** The secondary lasers are slung beneath the vehicle, one below the forward cabin/main body and the other below the rear end of the truck. Each can rotate 360 degrees and the barrels can be raised or lowered in a 45 degree arc of fire. They cannot strike at the same target as a dual shot, but can be trained to strike the same target independently (counts as two separate attacks). Typically, these weapons are controlled by the copilot or left on automatic.

Primary Purpose: Defense.

Secondary Purpose: Anti-Missile.

Mega-Damage: 4D6 M.D. per single blast.

Rate of Fire: Equal to the gunner's attacks/actions per melee round (typically 3 to 6), or 4 attacks per melee when automatically run by the on-board computer.

Maximum Effective Range: 2,000 feet (610 m).

Payload: Effectively unlimited.

Bonuses to Strike: +3 when controlled by the on-board computer.

3. **Gunnery Positions (2; forward and rear):** Attached directly to the vehicle are two gunners' boxes, each resembling a basket or chest-high booth into which a light or medium power can fit. In a pinch, a gunner in body armor can use these positions as well. These positions have no weapon systems themselves, as the power armor pilots/gunners are expected to fire using their own weapons. The partial cover afforded by the "baskets" means that any attacker firing upon the gunner must make a called shot to do so and is -3 to strike.

Typically, X-10 Predator power armors or similar units are used. Gunners with jet thrusters or jet packs can exit the position in a single action by leaping clear of the vehicle. Depending on the speed at which the hover truck is moving, however, getting back in may prove to be more challenging.

4. **Gunner Port (1):** While technically not a weapon system, this port is important to note as it allows the copilot to extend a rifle-sized or smaller weapon outside the cabin/main body to fire. Only targets within a 45 degree arc of the front of the vehicle can be attacked from this position.

5. **Sensors of Note:** Long-range communication, radar, and radar tracking same as standard robot vehicles.

Punch Guns

Created by Charles Daniel Christopher

One of the more unusual creations of Castle Electronics is the "punch gun." This forearm weapon is designed to be attached to power armors or used by 'Borgs. D-Bees with supernatural strength and Juicers also find them to be useful weapons.

These forearm weapons are designed with a special, dual trigger mechanism that allows them to be fired as a standard gun, similar to the 'Borg arm weapons found in the **Rifts** main book. However, they can also be set to activate when the arm they are mounted on is used in a successful punch! The knuckles of that particular hand are equipped with a special impact trigger that activates the weapon. This unusual system gives the wielder more versatility and can often catch an opponent by surprise during hand to hand combat.

There are a few limitations to the weapon. First, they cannot be used in conjunction with any other weapon attached to the same arm (including forearm blades and neural blaster gauntlets – see below). Secondly, while in "punch" mode, the weapon CANNOT be fired independently of a punch. However, the owner of the weapon can switch back and forth between "gun" and "punch" modes with no difficulty (counts as a single melee action). Finally, if the weapon is not used on power armor, where it can be linked to the power supply, these guns require an external power source, usually E-Clips.

The weapons are built to lie along the length of the forearm, with any E-Clip used pointing back towards the elbow. This is to ensure balance and to minimize weight problems when fighting in hand to hand combat. Still, the wielder will suffer a penalty of -1 to parry and dodge unless the weapon has been installed in a suit of power armor, in which case there is no penalty. Also, these weapons often have only a very limited range. Since they were designed to be used in close combat, the emphasis was put on power, not distance.

Using the weapon in "punch" mode means that whenever the user scores a successful punch, i.e. it is not parried or dodged, the gun will discharge, striking the target at the same time. Such an attack counts as a single melee action and does not require a second roll to strike. Since the secondary blast occurs at the same time as the punch, it cannot be parried or dodged.

Weapon Types, Mega-Damage & Range

Single Barrel Laser: 3D6 M.D., Range: 500 feet (152 m), Cost: 25,000 credits.

Double Barrel Laser: 4D6 M.D., Range: 800 feet (244 m), Cost: 32,000 credits. Note: This weapon can only be used on power armors due to its size.

Ion Blaster: 3D6 M.D., Range: 400 feet (122 m), Cost: 22,000 credits.

Particle Beam: 5D6 M.D., Range: 400 feet (122 m), Cost: 45,000 credits.

The payload of each weapon will depend on the power source used. In all cases, the payload will be unlimited if attached to the nuclear power plant of an exoskeleton.

Single Barrel Laser: 20 shots from a standard E-Clip, 30 from a long E-Clip, or 50 from a FSE-Clip (Front Sliding E-Clip).

Double Barrel Laser: 20 shots from a standard E-Clip, 30 shots from a long E-Clip, or 50 from an FSE-Clip.

Ion Blaster: 10 shots from a standard E-Clip, 20 from a long E-Clip, or 30 from an FSE-Clip.

Particle Beam: 6 from a short E-Clip, 12 from a long E-Clip, or 15 from an FSE-Clip.

Standard bionic arm-mounted weaponry can also be altered to act as a Punch Gun (add 20% to the cost of the weapon to modify the trigger mechanism and the knuckles of the armor, bionic arm, or power armor). Any power armor with an existing forearm mounted weapon can have that particular weapon modified to act as a Punch Gun as well. The modification costs anywhere from 5,000 to 8,000 credits for an operator to install the second switch to the existing weapon system.

Note, however, that plasma weapons cannot be used in this manner. The "splash" of the plasma upon impact would damage the attacker's hand and forearm, causing half damage to the attacker as well as the victim. Rail guns and machine guns are rarely altered for use in this fashion, as they can only be set to fire a single round or, at most, a short burst when in Punch Gun mode, limiting their effectiveness.

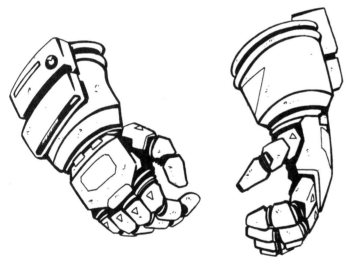

Neural Blaster Gauntlets

The technicians at Castle Electronics, unwilling to let the Gargoyles and Brodkil gain any technological advantage, have reversed engineered the blaster neural whip and have created their own version. Appearing as medieval gauntlets, they come in three varieties: a gauntlet-vambrace device that can be worn over normal body armor, a bionic attachment that can be built into the arms of a partial or full conversion cyborg, and an integral model that can be built into a powered armor or robot vehicle.

The smaller, worn models are still heavy and thus awkward to use unless the wielder has sufficient strength. Beings with

a P.S. of 21 or more can use them with no penalty, but those with a P.S. between 16 and 20 suffer a -2 penalty to strike, parry and dodge while using them. Those with a P.S. less than 16 cannot use the gauntlets as they will find them too awkward and heavy for hand to hand combat. There is no penalty for those models that are built into a power armor or robot vehicle.

In all cases, these gauntlets will release an electrical energy charge that temporarily short-circuits the nervous system of the victim. This energy is only released when the gauntlets are activated and the effect is delivered with a punch (the discharge points are built into the knuckles). There is a chance of rendering an unarmored person unconscious, but even if the individual remains conscious the charge will impair his movement.

Like the blaster neural whip, this weapon system is designed to kill and is meant to give NGR soldiers an advantage in hand to hand combat against the demonic hordes they face. Juicers, cyborgs and pilots of light power armors love these weapons as they are often overmatched by the Gargoyles and Brodkil on a one to one basis. The gauntlets help to even the playing field.

Physical damage from the gauntlets depends on the model used. The worn gauntlets inflict 1D6 M.D. in addition to any normal punch damage. The bionic version and those built into human-sized power armors inflict 2D6 M.D. in addition to normal punch damage. The large units built into robot vehicles inflict 3D6 M.D. in addition to the unit's normal punch damage. In all cases, there is a chance the victim will also be stunned.

Creatures which are vulnerable to electricity suffer double damage and are at -2 to save against being stunned. Creatures which are immune to electrical attacks suffer only normal punch damage and are not stunned by the energy discharge.

Stun Penalties for the Victim protected by half armor, magic armor or the Armor of Ithan spell: The body armor absorbs the Mega-Damage, but the character inside is still shocked and suffers the following penalties: -8 to strike, parry and dodge for 2D4 melees. The duration of the impairment is increased 2D4 melees for every hit by the gauntlets (also roll each time to see if knocked unconscious). Remember, stun is only effective against characters who are not protected by environmental armor.

Using this weapon against Mega-Damage beings such as demons and dragons will inflict the same amounts of Mega-Damage, but has different stun penalties. The jolt will cause the creature to only lose initiative and one melee action/attack per punch by the gauntlets. Save vs the Neural Blaster Gauntlets is the same as saving against non-lethal poison, 16 or higher. The character must save each time he is struck. A successful saving throw made by a Mega-Damage creature means that it is not stunned and only loses initiative.

Note: The gauntlets are ineffective against environmental M.D.C. body armor, power armor, and robots. It is effective against cyborgs not completely enclosed in full environmental armor, half suits of armor like those worn by the Gargoyles, or body armor without a helmet (it's not fully environmental without the helmet attached), Gargoyles, demons and other Mega-Damage creatures.

Payload: The worn gauntlets require an E-Clip to function, which slides into the vambrace portion of the unit. A short E-Clip provides 20 shots while a long E-clip provides 30 blasts. Note that a charge will only be used upon a successful strike. Any attack which is parried or dodged will not trigger the energy discharge and uses no power from the E-Clip.

The bionic version can either draw its power from an E-Clip in an arm port or can have a built-in capacitor that draws power from the cyborg's internal power supply. If an E-clip is used, a short clip provides 15 charges and a long clip provides 25. If the capacitor system is used, it will store enough energy for 30 discharges and recharges at a rate of one blast per melee round (every 15 seconds).

Both of the integral models used in power armors and robot vehicles draw their power from the units' power core and have an effectively unlimited payload.

Market Cost: The worn gauntlets sell for 15,000 credits. The bionic system costs 20,000 credits. The integral model for power armors costs 25,000 credits to install. The integral model for robot vehicles is 75,000 credits.

Adventures & Settings

Regarding New Oslo

As a dynamic and growing kingdom, New Oslo can serve as the basis of many campaigns and adventures. Most notable, of course, is the growing conflict between the forces of the fledgling nation and Fenrik, the Demon Wolf. Tracking down and defeating this monster can challenge even the most experienced heroes.

Across the Baltic, the armies of the Brodkil and Gargoyle Empires are on the move, threatening the New German Republic and all who stand with her, including New Oslo. Ewald von Dierks will not stand idly by while such menaces to his homeland remain strong. He will use every means at his disposal, openly and secretly, to make certain the NGR does not fall. He constantly works to support the continent and undermine the forces of darkness in Europe. On the flip side of that coin, the enemies of humanity in Europe have also noticed New Oslo and work towards its ruination. Both Ewald von Dierks and Thrace actively hire heroes and mercenaries to cross the Baltic to harass, spy on, and otherwise hamper the efforts of the Brodkil and Gargoyles.

Not all within the NGR are happy that the kingdom of New Oslo prospers either. Many feel that Ewald von Dierks has betrayed his people by elevating D-Bees beyond their "proper" place and hope to remove the current government and replace it with one more fitting to their human supremacist views. These factions are always looking for a means to discredit Ewald, Thrace or anyone who publicly supports this new nation's attitude towards nonhumans. Please note that these factions merely wish to remove the D-Bee "element" from society, and do not seek the complete ruination of New

Oslo and certainly do not wish to cause harm to the New German Republic.

Finally, the armies of the Warlords of Russia are bitter about how the rulers of the New German Republic have turned their back on them, and do not look too kindly towards this new power in the north. Worse still, those demonic forces that escape the purges of the Warlords may flee into the wilderness surrounding New Oslo, creating trouble for the outlying settlements.

Ironically, hunting and destroying these demonic "refugees" could serve as a basis for peace between the Warlords and New Oslo. Few things bring people together like a common enemy, and recognized villains who have escaped from Russia and are captured or destroyed in New Oslo definitely fall into this category. Clever adventurers could use such beings, sending either living prisoners or proof of their demise back to the warlords, as a public relations coup, portraying New Oslo as a kindred nation of survivors.

Wherever the adventurers may have hailed from, there is a great deal for them to deal with in the old Scandinavian lands, and only the best will survive the trials that are ahead of them.

Hook, Line & Sinker™ Adventures

Brodkil Everywhere

Hook: While adventuring within the borders of the Brodkil Empire, the group finds evidence of several military camps that have all been recently used. No sign of the monstrous occupants remains. Trackers in the group may notice that all the Brodkil were generally heading north, away from the human lands of Poznan and New Tarnow. Patriotic characters from the NGR will probably want to know what these monsters are up to.

Line: If the adventurers search for the Brodkil warriors, the trail will lead north to the edge of the Baltic Sea, where encounters with very aggressive, very *secretive* Brodkil will probably take place. It will quickly become clear that their enemies do NOT want to be followed and are working hard to eliminate any possible witnesses.

Sinker: Should the group survive encounters with the initial patrols, they will find the other warriors are encamped on the beach. Within a few hours, or sooner if the group is discovered, a Naut'Yll Red Trident Attack Submarine (see **Rifts Underseas**) will surface! The Naut'Yll have agreed to ferry the Brodkil across the Baltic so that they can begin raiding New Oslo and spread their reign of terror!

Does the group wage their own guerrilla war against the Brodkil? Do they notify the armed forces of the NGR or New Oslo? And how many other war bands have already been sent across the sea to the north? And just what are the Brodkil paying the Naut'Yll for their services?

The Natives Are Restless

Hook: The group finds itself hunting the mysterious attackers that have raided several of the outlying villages in the northern reaches of New Oslo. It seems that each winter, a number of the isolated settlements are methodically attack by monsters. While there have been only a few deaths, the villagers are getting very nervous. Something needs to be done before the next snow falls.

Line: While in the villages, the only clue the adventurers can find that links all of the attacks are a group of fur trappers and traders that have visited each settlement in the late summer.

Sinker: When the group catches up with the "mountain men" (which can take as long as the G.M. desires), they will be shocked to discover that they are not human at all, but werewolves! These savage brutes are forward scouts for the forces of Fenrik and spy out each village before planning the winter attacks. Destroying the shape-shifters will halt the attacks, at least for a time.

Refugees

Hook: While adventuring in the western edges of Russia, the group is contacted by some refugees seeking their help. They claim that their home was destroyed by one of the lieutenants of Warlord Burgasov when they couldn't afford the taxes demanded of them. They further claim that the Reavers in question are corrupt and seek to kill them and that their only hope of survival is to flee to New Oslo.

Line: If asked why they didn't appeal to their warlord for help against the rogue lieutenant, they will claim that the friends of the villain threatened their lives if they did. They feel they have no recourse except to flee Russia. (At this point, more suspicious characters may wonder why the refugees didn't flee south into warlord Romanov's lands.)

The refugees will pay the group well for their protection and escort, which will quickly become tested by scouts and Cossacks from Burgasov's forces. The group will be pursued by vengeful Reavers all the way to the Baltic. Furthermore, several heavy combat 'Borgs will be in the attackers' forces.

Sinker: By the time Warlord Burgasov's Cyborg shock-troopers arrive, the group will realize that the "refugees" are actually several powerful necromancers and their servants fleeing from Russia! If the group cannot clear their name, they will be accused by the Warlords of being in league with the Death Mages and hunted down like mad dogs!

Winter Games

Hook: The group is hired by some locals in New Oslo to hunt down a large pack of Hell Hounds that are raiding the area. While the militia would love to destroy these monsters themselves, they are needed to defend their town against further attacks. Unaffiliated adventurers, especially those seeking to make a reputation for themselves, are needed to go into the wildlands after the beasts.

Line: These particular beasts strike in well coordinated groups, harassing the adventurers whenever possible. They also try to lead the characters deeper into the wilderness of the northern lands.

Sinker: When the group is effectively isolated in the forests of northern Sweden, they will be mercilessly attacked by Fenry, werewolves, and other demons. The heroes will suddenly find that they have become the hunted!

The Unseen Enemy

Hook: If the group should prove themselves trustworthy, Thrace will hire them to go into the mountains of Norway in search of a potential nest of Gargoyles. More mercenary groups may respond to the bounty of 50,000 credits placed on any definite information of such a nest's location.

Line: The heroes are successful in finding the nest, but it only contains a handful of monsters (no more than 4 Gargoyles and perhaps a small clutch of eggs). However, an altar to some evil god will be found as well. Guarded by a Tectonic Entity, anyone who tampers with the shrine will be attacked. After a couple of melee rounds, especially if the entity loses its constructed body of sticks and stones quickly, the entity will flee. Any adventurer examining the altar will find that it has been used for several blood sacrifices. If a psychic performs an Object Read, it will reveal the image of a blood-stained wolf of great evil and power; Fenrik!

Sinker: The altar is dedicated to Fenrik, and he will become aware of the group either through their tampering with the shrine, or when the Tectonic Entity reports back to its master. The group will be tailed, and probably attacked by the minions of the dark god, on their way back to civilization.

The Price of Fame

Hook: If the heroes have successfully fought Brodkil or other monsters on the continent, they will be in for a surprise when they visit New Oslo. After only a couple of hours in any of the cities, the adventurers will find that they are minor celebrities, with some "fans" asking for their autographs.

Line: Soon the group will discover the source of their fame: they are featured on several advertisements for the military! Television commercials, magazines and billboards all sport the likenesses of the characters! It seems that during their last adventures in Europe, they were photographed by some scouts from New Oslo, and their images were used by the military as part of its latest recruitment drive that has been running for a couple of months.

Sinker: While the heroes can probably get their images removed from the ad campaign (or perhaps successfully demand a royalty fee), the damage will already have been done. For better or worse, they will be seen as supporters of the kingdom, meaning those with a score to settle with either Ewald von Dierks or New Oslo will consider the heroes potential targets. Worse yet, the Brodkil will know of the adventurers shortly, and place a substantial bounty on their heads!

Caught in the Middle

Hook: While working in the eastern portion of the kingdom, the heroes stumble upon a shipment of magical paraphernalia being shipped north. The items are obviously meant for use in a summoning ritual of some kind, and whatever is being summoned has the reek of the netherworlds on it! Good aligned adventurers will probably feel obligated to investigate. Selfish or evil characters can be hired by the local authorities to find out what is going on.

Line: The items were indeed meant for use in a summoning ritual. It seems that a high-level Shifter with an axe to grind has encamped on the ley line outside of New Oslo and is preparing to bring his demonic master to Rifts Earth!

Sinker: The heroes are not the only ones that have gotten wind of this matter. Fenrik has also found out, and is not eager to have any competition in this part of the world. He will *personally* lead a group of minions to find this Shifter and kill him! The dark god will follow the group quietly, allowing them to find the culprit. Fenrik wants to be certain he finds the ringleader of this plot and will generously allow the group to distract the Shifter's guards so that he may go for the heart of the matter. When the heroes find the Shifter, all hell will break loose! (The Shifter should be a least 7th level and have a number of bodyguards and low-level apprentices, levels 1D4+3.)

Fenrik will leap to the attack immediately, centering his full attention and attacks on the Shifter. He will leave his minions to kill anyone else in the area. Fortunately for the group, Fenrik will leave immediately after the Shifter is killed, but until then, the campsite will be the scene of a massive free-for-all with the adventurers caught in the middle of everything!

Setting the Stage... with the Stage Magician

Optional Material for Heroes Unlimited™

By Matt Reed

With a clap of thunder, lightning struck the stage, and from its midst, Bora the Elaborate, ever-present guardian of mischief and comeuppance, appeared from the smoke in the bolt's wake. The spotlights honed in on her, the camera crews worked to zoom in on her location. With a wave of her hand, the people cheered for her. "Good evening, Cascade!" She cried out, eliciting another round of cheers and applause. "I'll have to make this quick, my pretties, because the Mayor's bound to be siccing his cops on me."

A small chorus of boos followed her, which she waved away dismissively. "No, no, it's true... I'm a criminal." A soft smattering of cheers returned, "A hooligan." She continues, more of the audience responding to her words, "A vigilante. And as such, I've got a gift for everyone here. For I have some very special evidence that's going to show you all about who the real criminals are tonight..." With that, she produced a keycard, emblazoned with the insignia of Tychon Industries upon it. "Corporate executives really need to keep a hand on their wallets when dealing with coke-running death cults... Anyone could just walk off with their personal information."

The lights glittered, the camera phones were held high. It was her moment to expose the corruption, and illicit dealings of the city. She would be hunted, both by police and assassins, but it was worth it. Tonight, justice would be done, and nobody could silence her words...She was Bora the Elaborate, and for the first time in a long time, she felt like a hero.

Reconsidering the Stage Magician

The Stage Magician is an oft-neglected crime fighter in the world, especially with the flashy and powerful abilities of the bionic hero, the mutant, and the robotics. Where does the man with only skill and training come into play in a world such as this? The hero who uses guile and misdirection to confuse foes, and then capitalize on the advantage given, is one of a simpler time, a Silver Age hero in a modern world. There has always been incredible potential in the thinking man's hero, and after reading the wonderful write-up about the Ancient Weapon Master Specialist in **The Rifter® #74** by Robert Daley Jr, I realized that the Stage Magician could use a similar format. The question was clear, "How can the world's greatest illusionist fight crime?" As such, I've recreated this power category from the ground up.

There was a time in comics and television when the mentalist, the acrobat, and the escape artist all found their place. Using misdirection, their highly trained senses, and particular skill sets, they had an advantage over the villains and thugs of the world. These were the brave men and women who could scale walls, capitalize on surprise, paralyze someone with the sheer power of their presence, mesmerizing them. As the Silver Age gave way to the more Modern Age of comics, the stories of these plucky, innovative heroes gave way to the heroes with strange powers, or specialized armor. This article is meant to put the Stage Magician back into the limelight, his forte.

The first thing to recognize is that there are several styles of characters that can all qualify as Stage Mages. Cat burglars, pickpockets, acrobats, mind readers, and masters of disguise are all characters of stealth, finesse, and cunning. Some of them might wield a nimble short sword, a rapier, a bullwhip, or throwing knives. In general, their weapons are versatile, their tricks are incapacitating, and disorienting their foes is their single cause. As such, specific Styles have been developed to help emphasize each character's forte. Depending on the Style category selections and abilities therein, a Stage Magician can end up having a variety of abilities that lead to some

very interesting combinations to help enhance and flavor the Stage Mage.

Part of the Stage Magician's skill set involves a small bit of work with the G.M. There are simply times when a master of illusion, or a cunning mentalist, might have more foresight than even a canny player can muster. Certain tricks cannot be easily rationalized for those of us who have not intensively studied the stagecraft that these professionals can muster. As such, there are a few abilities that are considered to be 'open ended,' letting a player decide the situation or consequences on the spot, rather than carefully stating exactly what he's wearing, or what a certain trick is set to do. Rest assured, these scant abilities have this condition to capture the flavor of the power category, and are generally not considered to be easily abused or player fiat. Discuss the concept with your G.M. before selecting any of those powers to ensure ease of play.

A Note About Quality, Perception, and Contested Skills

In the abilities below, references will be made to the "quality" of a skill roll. A skill's quality is the actual number rolled, assuming the skill is successful. The quality of a skill roll is used in contested skills to determine success or failure for the parties involved. There will be a few elements of the Stage Magician's skill set that will influence skill quality, to give them an extra advantage in their actions, yet without making certain skills laughably easy to succeed at.

When dealing with Perception, it is advised to turn Perception into a percentile roll to better determine success and failure. My recommendation is to combine your Initiative and Perception bonuses, then multiply the result by 5%. Perception advances at every third level by 5%, as in Nightbane. This number can be very low, and players are encouraged to use skills they have, such as Surveillance, Detect Concealment, or Detect Ambush, instead of Perception if they have it. Consider Perception a default skill for characters without any specialized training to warrant those more professional skills.

A contested roll is a roll in which both characters involved are actively pitted against each other. Especially in a situation where only one person can succeed, such as hacking/protecting a computer system, stealth versus an alert guard, climbing to the top of a building first or any other sort of physical activity that relies on anything but sheer speed. When skills contest each other, both parties roll their skills. If both succeed, the skill with the higher quality wins.

Example:

Guardsman San Mercos pats down the disguised Stage Magician, and noted villain, Regalia Red, whom is disguised in the rags of an older woman. She has several weapons on her, concealed in the folds of her clothes, and foul intent in her eyes. The two characters contest their skills to determine who succeeds in their endeavor.

The Guardsman rolls a 10% on his Detect Concealment.

Regalia Red rolls a 53% on her Sleight of Hand, opting to use it for Concealment.

Both skill rolls are successes, but Regalia Red's gear goes undetected because she had the higher roll that was still a success. In this case, the "quality" of her roll was higher.

Certain abilities will actually boost the quality of a skill. While it does not increase the actual skill percentage itself, it adds to the chance of successfully using the skill when dealing with other people.

Example:

Young magician Bora the Elaborate sneaks across the second floor of an abandoned building. The sensor system below her has been ruled by the G.M. to have the equivalent of Advanced Hearing, and it is considered an 'active threat' which qualifies it for a contested skill roll.

Bora rolls a 6% on her Prowl, a success, but a very low roll. The sensor system rolls a 21% on its Advanced Hearing.

However, Bora has the ability of Master Burglar. This ability adds +20% to the "quality" of her Prowl rolls, changing her successful roll to a 26%.

Bora successfully eludes the sensor, at least for the moment.

The Revised Stage Magician Power Category

A professional illusionist or practitioner of legerdemain, a.k.a. sleight of hand. A master of disguise, impersonation, misdirection, and skulduggery. A normal person with a keen mind that keeps him two steps ahead of his foes, and when he has time to prepare ahead of time, he is elusive and deadly indeed.

The Stage Mage's predominant skills are Sleight Of Hand, which combines Palming, Concealment, and Pick Pockets into one skill; and Master of Escape, which combines Pick Locks and Escape Artist. Any skill roll needed for any of these skills may, and should, use Sleight Of Hand or Master of Escape instead.

Step One: The Usual

Attributes: As always, determine the eight attributes as usual, with these following bonuses:

+1D6 to M.A. (minimum 16)

+1D6+1 to P.P. (minimum 14)

+1D4 to P.B.

Hit Points: P.E. attribute +1D6 per level of experience.

S.D.C.: Determine the character's S.D.C. last, because it can be altered by skill bonuses. The character also gets a one-time bonus of 30 S.D.C.

Step Two: Education & Skills

Education is specialized, with the main emphasis around sleight of hand, illusion, disguise, and stage magic itself. Do not roll to determine education level nor skill programs.

Only the following skill areas are available to the Stage Mage.

Common & General Skills

Pilot: Automobile (+10%)
Pilot: One of choice (+15%; any).
Mathematics: Basic (+30%)
Language: Native Language (+25%)
Literacy: Native Language (+20%)
Language: One other language of choice (+15%).
One Ancient W.P. of choice, typically Thrown, Chain, or Sword.
Hand to Hand: Basic
And 2D4+3 Secondary Skills.

Sleight of Hand Skill Program

Card Sharp (+30%)
Sleight Of Hand – Stage Mage specialized skill – see below.
Master of Escape – Stage Mage specialized skill – see below.
Detect Concealment (+20%)
And two Rogue skills of choice (+10%).

Illusion & Magic Skill Program

Basic Electronics (+10%)
Dance (+10%)
Disguise (+20%)
Imitate Voices/Impersonation (+15%)
T.V. & Video (+15% when dealing with illusions and trickery)
Surveillance Systems (+10%, +20% when dealing with illusions & trickery)
Chemistry (+10%)
Ventriloquism (+30%)
Plus one scholastic Skill Program.
Equal to one year of college (+10%).

Special Skills

Sleight of Hand – 80% +1% per level

A skill that involves manual dexterity of hand and finger manipulation to perform certain feats. One of the basic tricks or gimmicks of Sleight of Hand is to distract the observer with one hand and otherwise manipulate the object with the other. Altogether, the skill includes Palming, Concealment, and Pick Pockets as one comprehensive skill, allowing you to use all three of those skills with a much greater chance of success. Together with the Style abilities below, Sleight Of Hand is the driving force that helps ensure surprise on the villains of the world.

Sleight Of Hand can be used to draw objects into the hand as a free action. With a single attack action, a Stage Magician can flourish some harmless legerdemain as a feint, intent on triggering the much-needed surprise over an op-ponent. Among its other uses, a successful roll to produce an item can open an enemy up to the many uses of Mentalism, or advanced abilities like The Turn, and the Prestige. In combat, Sleight Of Hand can be used to steal from a foe, or restrain him with handcuffs or other snares, all without the opponent's notice.

Master of Escape – 70% +2% per level

The legendary skill of Harry Houdini using body control, positioning, and lock picking to free oneself from bindings. Techniques include tensing and relaxing muscles, keeping joints flexible, basic contortionism, knot use, and hidden picks and tools. This skill combines Pick Locks, and Escape Artist as one comprehensive skill to emphasize the Stage Mage's skill and talent.

Penalties: The Stage Magician is an expert in these sort of situations, having practiced a hundred different combinations of knotwork, lock picking, and complications, sometimes all at once. Anyone else attempting to free themselves from these unusual situations takes three times as long. If there are any combination of circumstantial penalties, anyone other than a Stage Magician or Electronic Genius when applicable, take an additional -20% to their Escape Artist, or Locksmith rolls.

Escape and Lock Picking Penalties:

-0% Rope and knots, superior or otherwise: One melee (15 seconds).
-0% Key Padlock: 1D4 melees.
-5% Combination Padlock: 1D6 melees.
-10% Security Combination Padlock: 2D6 melees.
-0% Typical key lock, door or otherwise: 1D4 melees.
-5% Security key lock, door or otherwise: 2D4 melees.
-5% Currently Handcuffed: One melee.
-10% Currently Straightjacketed: 1D4+1 melees.
-0% Car trunk: 1D4-1 melees, (minimum 1).
-20% Vault door with a superior combination lock: 2D6 melees.
-40% Electric lock/bank vault: 6D6 minutes, and may require special tools.
-20% Lack of proper tools, must use inferior, improvised tools like a hairpin.
-50% No tools at all.

Doing research or practice of some of these abilities can help offset the penalties of a given task. Simply practicing the task at hand repeatedly, can negate up to -20% of penalties, or more up to the G.M.'s discretion. A task typically requires two hours per -10% of penalty you wish to negate.

Certain tasks, such as opening a bank vault, may require practicing on a dummy vault, or require welding gear or other specialized items. Such items may be considered cumbersome or exotic per G.M.'s discretion, otherwise all items are expected to be covered in the Stage Magician's gear bags, to be discussed in the Equipment Section.

Contortionism

The ability to temporarily dislocate bones from joints, fold and bend the body into extremely small areas or through spaces normally too tiny for a normal person. Can fold into a four foot ball and flatten self to four inches (10 cm). While the main bonus is already factored into Master of Escape, there are a few additional bonuses to factor in.

Bonuses:

Adds +2 to roll with punch, fall, or impact.
Adds +2 to defend against Hold or Lock attacks.
Adds +1 to strike on grappling attacks.

Juggling

The ability to toss up a number of objects such as balls, clubs, knives, torches, chainsaws, or any sort of usually small object, and keep them continuously up in the air. As a skilled expert, the practitioner develops a superior sense of coordination, manual dexterity, and reflexes which provide the following abilities and bonuses.

1. +1 attack per melee with a small thrown weapon at level one, three, six and nine. This can include darts, knives, javelins, sharpened cards, and other small items appropriate for throwing. Larger objects such as swords, chairs, or chainsaws do not receive the bonus attack.

2. +1 to strike with any thrown/missile weapon. +2 to called shot with any thrown/missile weapon. +1 to parry. These bonuses are in addition to hand to hand or W.P. Bonuses.

3. You may attempt to catch objects thrown at you, with both a successful parry roll, and Juggling check.

4. Number of items juggled: Up to six objects at level one, plus one for each additional level of experience. Base Skill 60% +5 per level of experience.

Step Three:

As a Stage Magician levels, he can select certain types of skills to aid his endeavors out in the world. Whether it be the crafty abilities of cold reading, or relying on a history of being an acrobat, the Stage Magician consistently learns new tricks to keep ahead of his foes.

At level one, a Stage Magician must select two styles listed below in addition to the General style, and the Bag Of Tricks style. From those four categories, he may gain any relevant Style Bonus if relevant, which may consist of a new skill or bonus, as well as eight abilities in total from the four Styles.

At level 3 you gain access to another Style, as well as the Advanced Style. You gain access to another Style at levels 5, 7, and 9. You gain two abilities from your selected styles at every odd level, starting at level 3.

In future articles, the Stage Magician may end up being able to cross-class with the other Special Training power categories, to dabble a bit in the life of a superspy or a manhunter, as well as the Ancient Weapon Master Specialist mentioned below. In these cases, the Stage Mage may pick one of the other categories instead of his own style, but must have more abilities from his actual power category than all other cross-training abilities combined.

The Styles

Advanced Style

As the Stage Mage grows in skill, new opportunities and advances become available, leading to some extraordinary signature moves in the Stage Magician's arsenal. This style becomes available at level 3.

Master of the Arts

Even other professionals are impressed with your speed and skill.

Rank 1: You halve the time to free yourself from restraints listed in the Sleight of Hand skill, down to a single melee action.

Nimbleness

You've perfected your avoidance tactics so that it becomes reflexive.

Rank 1: You gain the ability to Auto-dodge. If you already have this ability, it adds no further bonus.

Rank 2: You gain +1 to Auto-dodge.

Rank 3: You gain +2 to Auto-dodge.

The Pledge

Daggers, clubs, or cards. Always a nasty trick up your sleeve... always.

Rank 1: When subject to pat-downs or metal detectors, you may select one small, basic weapon on your body, of no more than six inches (15 cm) in length, to have been missed by the security sweep.

Rank 2: Even if you are stripped nude and thrown in a cell, you may still possess one basic weapon of no more than 2D6 damage, of no more than six inches in length. You may reveal this hidden weapon only once every 24 hours, and only if you've had the opportunity to gain a basic weapon. Example: If you've been in an empty hole for 24 hours and have already revealed your hidden weapon, you've had no opportunity to procure a new dagger.

The Turn

If you have a weapon, it's often best not to show that you have one until it is too late.

Rank 1: While initiating or engaging in combat, if you are unarmed and succeed at using sleight of hand to draw a weapon to your hand, your next attack gains a +2 to strike and +4 to damage with it. Anyone who sees this move take place is considered on guard for a similar trick and unable to be fooled by it for the rest of this combat. Producing and attacking with two weapons at once will net an additional +4 damage, but no further bonuses, no matter how many more ranks are taken.

Rank 2: Your surprise attack nets you a total of +4 to strike, and +6 to damage for this one attack. This bonus damage is not multiplied by multiple weapons thrown, nor by critical hits.

Rank 3: Your surprise attack nets you a total of +6 to strike, and +8 to damage for this one attack. This bonus damage is not multiplied by multiple weapons thrown, nor by critical hits.

The Prestige

Requires The Turn. A good stage mage can capitalize on a foe's confusion for a deadly assault, either with a sucker punch, or a thrown blade. In addition to the regular forms of surprise, being assaulted by 'The Turn' is also applicable here.

Rank 1: When dealing a surprise attack on a foe, the first melee or thrown attack of the combat deals double weapon damage. Any foe that sees this assault, or survives the initial attack, is unable to be struck in the same manner for the rest of the fight. When hitting a foe with multiple weapons simultaneously, multiply only one weapon's damage.

Rank 2: This surprise attack deals triple weapon damage.

Rank 3: This surprise attack deals quadruple weapon damage.

Wealth

It has often been said that the best super power is money. Petty cash is assumed to be just that, what you have on hand to work with, and not to be considered a workaround to budget your own power armor usage. Subject to G.M. allowance, you may occasionally be able to access up to ten times the amount of petty cash for larger, ongoing projects.

Rank 1: In your home city, you are considered to live very well, with a well-furnished home, workshop, and three cars. You always have petty cash of 2D4x1000 dollars available for the month.

Rank 2: You have homes scattered throughout a country of your choice, each one complete with all the vehicles, and standard gear necessary for your adventures. (The exact amount to be left up to the G.M.) You always have petty cash of 1D4x10,000 dollars available for the month.

Rank 3: You have homes all over the world, each one with all the standard gear for your adventures. (The exact amount to be left up to the G.M.) Your monthly petty cash increases to 2D4x30,000 dollars.

Bag of Tricks Style

Every Stage Magician, at his heart, deals with gadgets with a wide variety of uses. While most can simply be bought for use in the field, there are those who focus or enhance their gear for even greater results. When taking an Upgrade ability, it is considered from then on, that every time you replenish your supply of items, that they possess this upgraded ability.

Cold at Heart

You consider advanced optics to be cheating, and have leveled the playing field.

Rank 1: While in your costume which has at least half of its armor remaining, enemies using thermal vision to track you have a -20% to their detection skills.

Rank 2: While in your costume which has at least half of its armor remaining, you do not show up on thermal vision, not even your breath.

Persistent Gear

You always make sure to stock up on your best tricks of the trade.

Rank 1: Select one piece of equipment in the list below, or consult with your G.M. for any other item of use. You generally carry four of the appropriate item, or 20 if it is a small item like throwing stars, as part of your standard kit. Anytime you have some down time and can replenish your stocks, you can refill your supply without cost. You may select this ability multiple times, both for the same item, and for other items to always have an arsenal at your disposal.

Upgrade: Clinging Smoke

Simply running from the darkness does little to avail your enemies.

Rank 1: Anyone exposed to the initial blast of one of your smoke bombs gets their clothes coated by the same substance, which emits more blinding smoke about them, even if they flee the initial cloud. They are considered to be blinded for up to 3 minutes while outside the smoke cloud.

Upgrade: High Quality Snares

You've modified your snares to last longer, ensuring your enemies won't be limping away that easily.

Rank 1: Your Snares now hold a foe longer. More stable than the initial snare, the S.D.C. of the item is increased to 30 S.D.C., and wriggling out if it now takes 1D4+2 melee rounds. A successful Escape Artist roll still frees the target in two actions. High Quality Snares no longer fall apart on their own.

Upgrade: Scattering Glue Bombs

Not even the walls are safe from this powerful adhesive.

Rank 1: When you set off a glue bomb in a small area, such as a hallway, thin, but powerful strands of the glue are formed across the walls, floor, and ceiling, creating a haphazard series of obstacles for people to deal with, akin to spider webbing. It is still possible to venture through the affected space, but at no greater than a movement speed of 6.

Upgrade: Screeching Strobe Lights

As if it wasn't disorienting enough, suddenly a thousand decibel whine ripped through their midst.

Rank 1: Your Strobes now add a high-powered, deafening noise in addition to their lights. Verbal communication is impossible within 60 feet (18.3 m) of the Strobe, as well as skills that require concentration of any sort. Victims caught in the radius must make a saving throw vs nonlethal poison every round or immediately lose half of their attacks, and initiative.

Upgrade: Shocking Snares

A perfect aid in subduing and capturing all sorts of foes, combining restraint and a stunning jolt.

Rank 1: Your Snares now emit a stunning shock upon impact. If a victim is struck by the Snare, he takes 1D6 electrical damage, and must immediately make a saving throw vs non-lethal poison or get stunned, taking a -6 to all combat attacks in addition to the restraint. The stunning effect lasts as long as the person is caught by the snare, (usually four rounds).

Upgrade: Retching Gas Bombs

More foul than sour milk, it brings grown men down to their knees.

Rank 1: Your Stinking Gas Bombs now actively force those in their area to vomit. Those who fail to make a saving throw vs nonlethal poison now lose all but one of their attacks every round they are in the gas, and lose any automatic defenses for the duration until they can flee. Even those who make their saving throw lose half of their attacks and suffer a -6 to Initiative for the first round.

Cat Burglar Style

Some Stage Magicians use their legerdemain to take up the role of a thief. By all accounts, it would be simple to take the knowledge of misdirection, palming, and security systems in a bold new direction. By taking this style, you either gain Acrobatics or Prowl, or receive a +10% bonus to Palming, Prowl, and Acrobatics.

Breaking and Entering

Motion detectors, sensors, microphones, they all lack that human element needed to catch you.

Rank 1: You gain a +10% bonus to all skills needed when attempting to evade unmanned security systems, such as laser grids or security cameras.

Rank 2: You gain the ability to abort a failed roll regarding overriding or sabotaging surveillance systems. Any time you fail a roll to physically evade security, whether by prowl, surveillance, or such, once per day, you may choose to abort the attempt. You may not attempt to try the skill roll again for the rest of the day. Any attempt to do so will result in an automatic failure.

Rank 3: You have one more chance to abort a failed roll in this nature per day.

Fast Hands

Even with your life on the line, you've always got a little bit more panache than most. These actions work best when dealing with foes in melee.

Rank 1: You gain a single non-combat action a round to be used solely for the art of misdirection, pick pocketing, or such.

Rank 2: You gain a second non-combat action of this nature.

Rank 3: You gain a third non-combat action of this nature.

Master Burglar

You've joked with friends that you can open a lock bare-handed, and someday, you'll prove it to them.

Rank 1: You gain a +20% to the quality of your contested prowl rolls.

Rank 2: You no longer take penalties for picking locks without proper tools or improvised tools. However, the time it takes to pick locks in this manner is doubled.

Light Fingers

You were never anywhere near the criminals, and yet you ended up with all of their wallets...

Rank 1: The range at which you can pick pockets increases by 1 foot (0.3 m) per level. You must have surprise on your side to use this ability.

Rank 2: The range of this ability is increased to 2 feet (0.6 m) per level.

Rank 3: The range of this ability is increased to 3 feet (1 m) per level, up to a maximum of 30 feet (9.1 m).

Wall Crawler

The skylight is always preferable to the front door.

Rank 1: As long as you have the proper gear, you only need to roll Climb every 40 feet (12.2 m) you ascend, as opposed to every 10 feet (3 m).

Rank 2: You may fight from a wall or ceiling with no negatives, provided you are using the proper gear. Any penalties you may incur for climbing in dangerous conditions, injuries or such, are all halved.

Circus Performer Style

By selecting this style, you gain a skill in either Tumbling, Gymnastics, or Acrobatics, or a +10% bonus to any one of those skills. You also gain the ability to fall 10 feet (3 m) without taking any damage, 20 feet (6 m) if you jump on your own accord.

Acrobalance

You've learned to stand very still in extraordinarily rigorous positions.

Rank 1: You may maintain a stance as a living statue for one hour + 15 minutes per level. In addition, you gain a bonus of +5% to Prowl , due to being able to hold your position over a door, or in other rigid positions where slight movement might give you away. +2D6 to S.D.C., +1 P.S. and +1 P.E. for the ruthless training.

Antipodism

You've mastered balancing things on your feet to an impressive degree.

Rank 1: When you use your legs to throw opponents in melee, you are +2 to Throw doing 2D6 damage, and the victim loses his next attack and initiative as normal.

Rank 2: Your Throw bonus increases to a +4 as well as another +4 to damage on these throws, and the victim loses two attacks and initiative.

Rank 3: Your Antipode Throw defense is now considered an auto-defense.

Beast Tamer

When you stare into the eyes of a predator, you are the one that comes out on top.

Rank 1: You gain the Animal Husbandry skill, or a +20% bonus to it if you already have it. On a successful roll, you may calm an aggressive creature to an indifferent state. Enraged creatures may still be aggressive and territorial, but will opt to at least delay combat for a few scant moments as the Stage Magician holds them at bay. Any hostile action to the creature or otherwise provoking it, such as stealing its eggs, will instantly snap it out of its lulled state, and make it immune to any further soothing. The stages go as such, Enraged, Aggressive, Indifferent, Curious, Docile, Protective.

Rank 2: A successful Animal Husbandry roll will force the animal to move two stages towards Docile.

Breakfall

Years of experience and training have honed your instincts to lessen the trauma of a fall.

Rank 1: Breakfall is the more advanced version of Roll with Punch/Fall/Impact. The character takes no damage from a fall if the Breakfall is successful, and only half damage if the roll fails. The bonuses start off at a +2 to Breakfall.

Rank 2: Your bonuses with Breakfall are now +4.

Rank 3: Your bonuses with Breakfall are now +6.

Bullwhip Expert

Taming lions, scaring criminals, the bullwhip has a variety of uses, and you know them all.

Rank 1: You gain a +10% to Animal Husbandry in regard to work animals and circus-trained animals. You also have learned how to defend yourself with one, garnering the ability to auto-entangle as a defense using the same bonuses to strike garnered by the weapon proficiency. You also gain +2 to disarm and entangle with a whip. You may also use your whip to swing short distances, 30 feet (9.1 m) or less, and automatically unsnare your whip from its swing point.

Rank 2: Your bonuses increase to a +4 to disarm and entangle with a whip.

Rank 3: Your bonuses increase to a +6 to disarm and entangle with a whip.

Exceptional Acrobat

An exceptional and rigorous lifestyle has left you with a skill set far beyond the standard gymnast.

Rank 1: You gain an additional +20% to all gymnastic, tumbling, and acrobatic moves. Any penalties for such moves are halved. The range you can fall or jump down without damage increases by 10 feet (3 m).

Rank 2: You gain a +4 to roll with a fall, +4 to Maintain Balance, and your gymnastic, acrobatic, and tumbling skills may now surpass 98% as per the Hardware skills.

Kip Up

With a quick flex of the legs, you hop right back up, eager for more.

Rank 1: From a prone position, you may stand up without taking an attack.

Master Juggler

While most Stage Magicians can juggle well, your skill has surpassed even them.

Rank 1: At the cost of your Automatic Defense, you may use your parry bonus to catch a muscle-powered projectile. You may also handle small objects on fire without damage, provided you throw them as your next attack. Normally, this requires a Juggling roll, as well as a successful parry.

Rank 2: You receive a +2 to your Parry roll, and may catch two objects simultaneously.

Rank 3: You receive a +4 to your Parry roll, and it is now considered an Auto-Defense.

General Style

Despite their myriad of differences, all Stage Mages have some common core qualities as they advance and develop their own fighting style.

Blind Fighter

Given the magician's elusive nature, you've trained to fight with obscured sight.

Rank 1: You only suffer half the penalties for being blinded in combat, both ranged and melee, usually a -8 to all combat rolls. You may not take any ability from cross-class training that has a similar ability.

Rank 2: All penalties due to blindness in melee, are reduced to -1 only. Ranged combat is unchanged.

Efficient Quiver

You rarely run low on your thrown weapons.

Rank 1: As with the Ancient Weapon Master Specialist, you can fit twice as many ranged weapons into your quiver or holster. For those using a deck of cards, you may fit 104 cards into a standard deck slot. You may not take Efficient Quiver a second time through cross-class training or through the Master Thrower Style.

Entangler

You were made to improvise in combat, much to your foes' confusion.

Rank 1: You gain +2 to Entangle foes.

Rank 2: You gain +3 to Entangle foes, and it is considered an auto-defense for you.

Rank 3: You gain +4 to Entangle foes.

Expert Observer

You know just the right places to look for just about anything that people like to hide.

Rank 1: The quality of your successful skill rolls for Detect Concealment and Detect Ambush increases by 20%.

Expert Legerdemain

You are a magician's magician, even able to fool others in the art.

Rank 1: The quality of your successful skill rolls for Sleight of Hand involving picking pockets and palming increases by 20%.

Expert Card Sharp

Anyone who sits at the card table with you is just another mark... and a fool.

Rank 1: The quality of your successful skill rolls for Card Sharp increases by 20%.

Grace Under Pressure

Some people break under pressure, but you work your best under the clock.

Rank 1: You no longer take penalties to skill rolls for stressful situations.

Internal Quiver

Lessons of muscle control from the Great Houdini still hold a lot of merit.

Rank 1: The Stage Mage gains the ability to swallow small, indigestible items to regurgitate later, unharmed. The object must be small enough to completely swallow, and he can only hold about a handful in his stomach. It takes one attack to swallow, two attacks to retrieve, and a full melee round to covertly retrieve. Unless properly secured, bladed weapons are completely inadvisable.

Oldest Traditions

You've devoted yourself to some of the older traditions of entertainment, held by bards, storytellers, and performers of all types.

Rank 1: You may gain three skills of the following: Singing, Rope Use, Storytelling, one Lore skill, or a Play Instrument skill, all at +10%.

Showstopper

Even the stage itself can be a valuable asset to your more heroic endeavors. From making it rain in the desert, or disappearing bridges, this ability is central to the Stage Magician's arsenal if he wants to be seen and heard.

Rank 1: Given an hour's setup time, you can produce a show that can bewilder and amaze passers-by. While the show may have a variety of uses per G.M. discretion, the most obvious use is that the gathered crowd and command of the situation can act as a screen to assist other conspirators in the area. While within the Showstopper, active observers are -20% to all skill rolls involving detection or perception. Larger scale displays may require more time, per G.M.'s discretion.

Now any Stage Magician can put on a show of wonder and amazement that can leave the audience spellbound. This ability is for those who have figured out how to use their imagination and talent to detain or injure members of the audience, for good or for ill.

You can prepare an area for illusionary work of a size equal to a small gymnasium, about 60 feet (18.3 m) square. You must have access to this area for an hour, and skill rolls may be required to discreetly set up traps in advance. What and where these traps are, is left up to the player's description. Your base of operations is assumed to be trapped in a similar style.

When completed, you may, with a single attack, perform any of these moves, a total of six times. Attack rolls needed to damage, knock prone, or otherwise affect people are done solely with a strike bonus of +6. Any attack requiring a saving throw uses a basic saving throw vs a 14 versus with G.M.'s discretion of P.E. or M.E. bonuses. As for the type of abilities, you may:

- Force the people in a twenty foot (6 m) radius to make a saving throw vs a Horror Factor of 12.
- Damage people in a five foot (1.5 m) radius for 3D6 damage of any basic damage type, such as impact, fire, or electricity.
- Blind people within 30 feet/9.1 m (saving throw; see above), for 2D4 rounds.
- Stun people within 30 feet/9.1 m (saving throw; see above), for one round.
- Knock everyone prone within 60 feet (18.3 m).
- Attempt to net or snare everyone in an area of 15 feet (4.6 m).
- Move yourself to another place within the prepared area. This action takes three melee attacks.

Rank 2: When preparing a Showstopper, you may perform any of the listed moves up to twelve times, instead of six.

Rank 3: When preparing a Showstopper, you may perform any of the listed moves up to a whopping eighteen times, instead of six.

Quick Feet

You can always slip away at top speed, when the situation requires it.

Rank 1: Your speed is no longer halved when Prowling.

Slow Metabolism

Some feats of stage magic require the magician to be able to regulate his body into a near-death state, and you have practiced these arts.

Rank 1: With one full minute of concentration, you can slow your heartbeat and metabolism to a crawl as per the psionic ability of Death Trance with a duration of 4 hours per level.

Master Thrower Style

The true signature of the Stage Magician is the light, thrown weapons. Deft hands that sling a blade of steel, or a razor sharp card with but a mere flick of the wrist. By selecting this style, you gain your P.S. damage bonus with thrown weapons, or an extra attack per round with thrown weapons. Your weapon selection must be a light, one-handed weapon. You may not select more than half of your abilities from this style and the Master Of Blades style.

You may select abilities from the Ancient Weapon Master Specialist for Ranged or General abilities on a one to one basis, but you must select one specific throwing weapon to use.

Finesse

It's all in how you throw it.

Rank 1: Instead of using your P.S. bonus for damage with ranged weapons, you can opt to use your P.P. to determine the damage bonus instead, capping at +8. Also available as an Ancient Weapon Master Specialist ability.

Master of Blades Style

Some Stage Mages prefer a more elaborate, but no less theatric approach to combat by choosing a melee weapon to specialize in. By selecting this style, you gain an extra attack per round with your chosen weapon. Your weapon selection must be a light, one-handed weapon or a staff. Sword canes, chains, and staves are predominant weapons for the melee-Stage Mage. You may not select more than half of your abilities from this style and/or the Master Thrower style.

You may select abilities from the Ancient Weapon Master Specialist for Melee or General abilities on a one to one basis, but you must select one specific melee weapon to use. See **The Rifter® #74**, page 30, for the Ancient Weapon Master Specialist

Mentalist Style

The Stage Mage that studies mentalism, studies the way we think and how to glean information through subtle details, much like fortune tellers. An experienced mentalist is one who can make an instant analysis of a person upon first glance through body cues, nervous tics, and calculated guessing, then implant a thought into their head to manipulate the victim to his whim. By selecting this style, you gain either the skill of Psychology +10%, or Fast Talking +10%, OR add a +10% to one of those skills if you already possess it. Most Mentalism skills require a Psychology roll as well as a saving throw vs psionics with M.E. bonuses, as standard. Victims of Mentalism are considered to have their guard up against such tricks after they discover what happened to them, and are immune to such tricks for the next 24 hours. In addition, characters over level 5, or who are Master Psychics, are automatically immune to such trickery, as they have much more disciplined minds. As with most abilities, each of these actions takes a single attack to perform.

Eidetic Memory

A disciplined mind is the greatest weapon.

Rank 1: The Stage Magician gains the equivalent of the psychic ability of Total Recall for use up to six times a day with no I.S.P. cost.

Rank 2: The amount of uses of this ability increases up to twelve times a day.

Hypnotic Suggestion

Requires Mentalism as a prerequisite. The human mind is susceptible to a great many messages and images, but only in that brief moment when you can catch them off guard. A great deal of Stage Mages use this ability during one of their actual tricks to force their audience to act as they choose.

Rank 1: When a subject is surprised or entranced, a stage magician may use a combination of physical demeanor, his powerful presence, and a choice phrase to momentarily exploit a person's mindset. When they have surprise on their side, the Stage Mage may roll Psychology. If they succeed, they may then implant a single hypnotic suggestion into the victim's mind, as per the psychic power with a saving throw vs psionics. Each person may only have one suggestion implanted at a time, and the victim is not likely to remember the attempt, unless the Stage Mage goes out of his way to call attention to it, such as gloating about it later.

Knowing the Audience

Requires Mentalism as a prerequisite. Personality mimicry, calculated responses, and a bit of charm can open many doors.

Rank 1: After succeeding at a Psychology roll, and taking some time to size up a suitable mark for 5 minutes, a charming Stage Magician gains a +10% bonus to his social skills (psychology, fast-talking, charm, seduction, etc.) when dealing with that person and those of similar mindset (e.g. thugs, jocks, businessmen). This ability lasts until the end of the conversation.

Rank 2: The bonus increases to +20%.

Mentalism

Just by studying human nature and calculated responses, you've learned how to read a person's most likely responses.

Rank 1: By taking this ability, you may roll Psychology to 'cold read' a person, gleaning some general, but useful information from them. This ability can be attempted up to five times a day.

Rank 2: The amount of uses per day increases to 10.

Rank 3: The amount of uses per day increases to 15.

Ordered Mind

A firm grounding in identity and self helps one to shrug off mental effects.

Rank 1: You now make a saving throw versus psionics as a Minor Psionic, 12 or above needed.

Entrance Others

Requires Mentalism as a prerequisite. Instead of a hypnotic suggestion, a magician may choose to simply entrance someone with their mesmerizing gaze or item of note, as in the

Trance spell. Again, surprise of a form, and a successful roll for Psychology are needed to ensure susceptibility, and victims may attempt a saving throw vs psionics to shake off the initial attack.

Rank 1: The ability to entrance victims can be used three times a day.

Rank 2: The ability to entrance victims can be used six times a day.

Rank 3: When using Entrance, you may affect up to six people as a single attack, who all have a clear line of sight to you and can hear you, simultaneously.

Telepathy

Requires Mentalism as a prerequisite. A cunning Stage Magician can glean even more from a target, almost as if he were reading their mind.

Rank 1: The Stage Magician may emulate the spell Zone of Truth when interrogating a victim, for a total of four 'yes or no' questions. For this ability to work, the victim must make a saving throw vs Psionics as above, failure indicates that the victim unintentionally relayed critical information to the Stage mage. This ability may be used one time a day.

Rank 2: The amount of uses per day increases by one, to a total of two.

Rank 3: The amount of uses per day increases by one, to a total of three.

Thousand Faces Style

One of the variants of the Stage Magician are the vaunted quick-change artists, people who can, in a single moment, completely change what they wear. By selecting this style, you gain the skill of Acting. As an alternative, you can gain a +10% bonus to Disguise, Impersonation, or Acting, if you already have it.

Forensic Foil

The police always have had a hard time tying you to any crime scene.

Rank 1: As long as you are in costume, you cannot leave fingerprints. Your costume helps thwart attempts at computer recognition, playing off of facial recognition software. You also tend to carry forensic foiling devices to help spoil investigations. When you spend 30 minutes spoiling a 30 foot (9.1 m) area, all attempts at forensics and security analysis are made at -15%.

Rank 2: The penalty for forensic work and security analysis to track you increases to -30%.

Quick-Change Artist

From exceptional to everyday, all in the blink of an eye.

Rank 1: You can change your clothing up to three times a day with but a melee attack. You do not need to declare your outfits at the start of a day unless it is of special significance, like a specific style of uniform. Body armor must be removed before doing a Quick Change.

Rank 2: Taking this ability again allows you an additional three times a day of quick change, as well as an extra +10% to Disguise, Impersonation, or Acting. You also have enough connections and backers to allow you a wide array of costumes and outfits to allow you to fit in almost anywhere in the world, though you may have to spend some time gaining access to them.

Impersonation

Requires Quick-Change Artist as a prerequisite. Much like the ninjas of old, you've learned how to quickly assume a new role convincingly.

Rank 1: You gain +10% to the Impersonation skill. In one melee round and out of sight, you can roll Impersonation to assume a new basic identity (though clothing may require a Quick-Change) believable to all but the closest scrutiny. General types of basic identities are tourist, businessman, the elderly, street punk, and nondescript citizen.

Rank 2: Your new identity is so convincing that even telepaths are initially fooled by it. Anyone using Telepathy on you must actively keep scanning your surface thoughts for a number of minutes equal to your level +1 in order to discover you're not who you are pretending to be.

Faking It

Requires Quick-Change Artist as a prerequisite. So you may not know much about advanced warfare tactics, wood sculpting, or open-heart surgery, but you can wing it in a conversation at least, and sometimes all three topics at once.

Rank 1: When in disguise, the Stage Magician may emulate having specific knowledge of a skill needed if he succeeds at an Impersonation check. While the Stage Mage may not actually HAVE the skill of note, he can talk the talk with enough confidence to pass casual scrutiny. Only under intense or specific scrutiny does the guise falter.

Face Masks

There's no need to wear a mask if nobody knows your real face.

Rank 1: You are generally considered to be wearing a facial disguise. The mask can be sculpted to have anywhere from an ugly to a beautiful visage, (max P.B. 16). Given an hour of time, you may create a mask of anyone you have proper photographs of.

Rank 2: Your disguise equipment can copy retinal scans, and fingerprints, provided you can supply the proper information. After studying a target's voice for an hour, with a successful Imitate Voices roll, you can fool voice analyzers (by audiotaping him for his voice patterns, lifting fingerprints, catching a scan of his eyes while he's unconscious, and similar methods).

Identity Crisis

Everyone knows you as someone, but they tend to differ on who you really are.

Rank 1: You possess two cover identities that stand up to basic scrutiny, i.e. checking tax records, bank statements, living arrangements.

Rank 2: You possess four cover identities, one of which actually garners you leeway into a corporation or government agency, meaning that you could be verified as an FBI agent, or a little-seen Vice President of Marketing in a large conglomerate business, per G.M. discretion.

Rank 3: You possess eight cover identities, three of which may be planted into large corporations or agencies. Each identity can only be exposed with careful, long-term scrutiny.

Physical Mimicry

Requires Faking It and two other Thousand Faces abilities as a prerequisite. Your body control has been so perfected that you can follow the exact motions of another person.

Rank 1: When observing another person, you may perfectly mimic one short (15 seconds) sequence of motions that they perform, enough so that you may replicate the sequence. Whether it be a complicated dance, a cautious step through a minefield, or entering a key code, you can perfectly replicate the movement and garner the same success. If a stealthy ally uses Prowl to shift over some squeaking boards, you may mimic the motions to succeed without a roll. This ability must be used within five minutes of viewing the attack, and the situation must not have changed. As with our previous example, if a board had fallen over after the first person prowled through, then this ability may not be used as the situation has changed. Physical Mimicry may be used twice a day.

Rank 2: You may use Physical Mimicry three times a day.

Rank 3: You may use Physical Mimicry four times a day.

All other aspects of the Stage Magician are unchanged.

Equipment and Gear Suitable for the Stage Magician

The Stage Magician is assumed to be familiar with all the items listed below, as in how to use, build, and store such various gadgets. Characters of other Power Categories may have the same familiarity with them as well, per G.M. discretion.

A variety of these items are listed generically, allowing the Stage Mage to interpret his arsenal in whatever manner he chooses. Given the Magician's fixation on the elaborate, it is entirely possible to use your gadgets to create a display of power and awe. Fire traps could be set up to represent Chinese dragons made of flame, snares could be visualized as simple handcuffs targeting a foe's arms, clouds of smoke could shift colors as they obscure people. Of course, these items are simply gadgets, crafted and timed perfectly by their Magician, and do have limits as to how elaborate or otherworldly they may seem.

Vehicle Multitool

A small lifesaving device to assist drivers in vehicular crashes. Able to shred seatbelts in a single attack, it is also capable of destroying a standard windshield in a full round.

Also comes with a tiny flashlight and cellphone charger. **Cost:** $18 to purchase.

Damaging Trap

Basic anti-personnel traps that can inflict lethal damage. You can purchase or create them to inflict any basic attack type of damage: fire, impact, electricity, poison, etc. More high-tech damage types such as radiation, energy, or microwave are only available at the G.M.s discretion. Each trap generally does 4D6 damage with +6 to strike a single target. Your traps may be set off remotely or by trigger, such as motion, or tripwire. **Cost:** Varies, but generally about $30 per trap.

Glow Bombs

Essentially, day-glow paint balloons meant to splatter paint onto an enemy. While humiliating, the best aspect of simply throwing paint on someone is to mark them later, as well as help keep an eye on them in dark areas. Glow Bombs splatter over a five foot (1.5 m) radius, typically with a green or pink, bright neon paint, hitting 1D4+1 people in the area. People covered in the glowing paint find it nearly impossible to prowl in shadows, or get lost in a group. All such rolls are made at -40% until they can change clothes or otherwise remove the paint. Victims can be blinded by a glow bomb, requiring a successful called shot to the face. Paint smears over visors and face masks, and irritates the eyes. If the victim has no face protection he can remove, it will take 2D4 minutes to clear the eyes, or wipe the goggles free of such a nuisance. **Cost:** $3 per glow bomb.

Glue Bombs

Area denial weaponry of the non-lethal variety. Each glue bomb can cover an area of up to 30 square feet (10 m), and forces a saving throw vs non-lethal poison to all those who are in the area of effect, as well as those who enter the area later. Failure indicates that the victim must spend 1D4 melees struggling against the glue to leave the area. Success means that the victim must spend 1D4 melee attacks in order to leave the area. Glue bombs cannot impede robots, nor vehicles of any sort, though per G.M. discretion, a glue bomb into a car engine may deal a significant amount of damage to the vehicle. **Cost:** $8 per bomb.

Smoke Bombs

These small capsules, about the size of a large multivitamin, erupt into a thick smoke of any particular color, upon a hard impact. Each capsule can obscure a 30 foot (9.1 m) area with blinding smoke for 5 minutes, less if in strong winds. Smoke is also rather good at helping mute thermal imaging within the cloud. All forms of thermal vision give the user only a vague sense of the location of anyone within the cloud, reducing the penalties of blindness from -8 to -5. Called Shots are impossible, as well. **Cost:** $5 each.

Flash Bangs

Used by advanced tactical teams the world over, the flash bang produces a loud noise along with a disorienting bright light, and together they give a powerful, if momentary, advantage in combat. Victims within a 10 foot (3 m) range must make a saving throw of 16 or higher, using their P.P. bonuses, if any, as the victim tries to shield his eyes and ears before the flash bang goes off. Those who fail the saving throw are -8 to all combat attacks for 2D4 melee rounds, and have a 1-75% chance of falling per 10 feet (3 m) they try to travel. On a successful saving throw, the victim is not blinded, nor deafened. Those with both cybernetic eyes and ears are immune to flash bangs, and having either one but not the other cuts the penalties and duration in half. **Cost:** $40 to purchase, $20 to create home-made.

Thrown Snares

Whether a myriad of rings, handcuffs, or a 'magic' rope, you keep a steady supply of snares that help keep you from being outnumbered. A snare is ultimately a gadget that can take a variety of shapes, but all of which share the same function, to inhibit and detain someone. Anyone hit by a thrown snare is wrapped up in it as per a net, losing one attack and goes prone. Snare attacks have a high chance (70%) of catching a victim's arms, in addition to the legs. A victim of a snare must either break it by doing 20 S.D.C. to it, or spend 1D4 rounds attempting to free himself. A successful Escape Artist roll will free the victim in two attacks. **Cost:** Varies, but generally about $14 each.

Strobes

A constant flashing light that can be emitted as either a cone or in a radius. They are remarkably distracting, and a nuisance in combat. Most strobes are small, hockey puck-sized items that emit a rapid burst of light repeatedly that, when activated by hand or remotely, emits an incredibly distracting flashing light in a cone or radius of up to 20 feet (6 m). People in the strobe's area of effect are minus 10% to all Detection skills (such as Detect Concealment, Surveillance, etc), minus 2 to initiative, and minus one attack a round. In darkness, the strobe light provides minimal lighting, only reducing penalties for blindness by one point. Strobes last for 5 minutes before needing to be recharged. **Cost:** $10 each.

Holograms

A small holographic generator that can record input and project it back for a short period of time, about the size of a wallet. The hologram generator can record up to 30 seconds of data of an area of no larger than 20 feet (6 m) in diameter, and replicate the scene later remotely up to two times before needing recharged. Scenes of any sort can be recorded, whether it be a person falling to their death, a vehicle crashing towards the scene, a bomb ready to explode. Anyone with advanced optics or sensory input, such as Advanced Hearing, can tell that the visual image is illusory. Hologram generators are generally considered high-tech, and may be restricted, per G.M. discretion. **Cost:** Varies and may require TV & Video skills. $140 for a home-made projector.

Stinking Gas Bombs

Each capsule produces a misty cloud that covers a 10x10 foot (3x3 m) area. Everyone within the cloud must make a saving throw vs non-lethal poison, or lose half their attacks that round, are -3 to all combat rolls, and are forced to flee the cloud at their nearest opportunity. Those who make their saving throw lose two melee attacks and are -1 to all combat rolls for the duration they are in the cloud. **Cost:** $30 each.

Upgradeable Items

Fantoccini Wires

Micro-thin wires, used for puppetry originally, have their uses for the imaginative.

Rank 1: This wire harness set sits primarily on your back, but is secure enough to support your weight comfortably. The harness works primarily by using a series of wires that can be sent out of your sleeves or pants to manipulate your environment. You may manipulate your environment within 30 feet (9.1 m) using these wires for simple, basic tasks, such as knocking something aside, flipping a switch, or grabbing a small object, phone-sized or less, and drawing it to your hand. Drawing an item from your hand up your sleeve is considered a free attack, and can be done any number of times a round. You may also manipulate a puppet from a distance, as a full round action. **Cost:** $260.

Rank 2: You've refined your harness up to the point where, in addition to its other feats, it has become the equivalent of a spike and towline, with a range of 200 feet (61 m), and a lifting capacity of 500 pounds (225 kg). **Cost:** $6,000.

Heist Bag

A large backpack that contains a standard array of glass cutters, aerosol cans, fingerprint dust, and electronic tools. It is considered to have everything an aspiring Stage Mage needs in order to counteract basic surveillance, bypass locks, and do so quietly. The G.M. may rule that specific elements may be considered to be awkward to move, or of a specialized nature, such as cryo tanks, advanced tools, or inflatable pads.

Rank 1: Allows the character the chance to perform most, if not all, tasks associated with breaking and entering. Several contents of the bag are considered highly illegal to have in your possession. While elements of the heist bag may be usable in combat, the backpack is large and requires time and patience to use for skills, therefore any bonuses given by the gear bag are not factored in, during combat. **Cost:** $200.

Rank 2: Higher quality gear, some of which is more fine-tuned and specialized to ensure success. This bag adds a +10% to all heist-related skills when in use. **Cost:** $800.

Rank 3: Extraordinarily high-tech gear, some of which may be of alien origin, or otherwise Century Station technology. Sensor scanners and jammers, intricate laser scramblers, complete with a heads-up display that highlights all noted security systems. Almost everything in the bag is bound to be highly illegal, and considered 'super' paraphernalia, which may cause problems if the character is arrested. This bag adds a +20% to all heist-related skills when in use, as well as a +20% to the quality of those rolls. **Cost:** Varies, and may require extensive resources and connections, but could be found on the black market for $60,000.

Climbing Bag

A small backpack or waist bag, with harness, that contains all of the necessary items needed to scale a building, rock structure or elevator shaft. Generally comes with a 100 foot (30 m) length of rope for ease of rappelling.

Rank 1: While climbing can be attempted without any specialized equipment, there are many areas that are near impossible to climb without specialized gear. This gear bag allows you to attempt those climbs. **Cost:** $160.

Rank 2: Higher quality gear, with thin, carbon wire used for rappels instead of good rope, suction-cup gloves, and a low-dose combat cocktail to help the body resist tiring, and improve focus on those long climbs. Some items in this gear bag are considered paraphernalia for criminal activity. This bag adds a +10% to all climb rolls made. **Cost:** $820.

Rank 3: Extraordinarily high-tech gear, some of which may be of alien origin, or otherwise Century Station-level technology. Electro-Stick gloves, adhesion spray, liquid cable dispensers, so almost everything in the bag is bound to be highly illegal, and considered 'super' paraphernalia, which may cause additional problems if the character is arrested. This bag adds a +20% to all climb rolls made, and automatically negates up to -10% of penalties to any rolls made due to surface or weather conditions. **Cost:** Varies, and may require extensive resources and connections, but could be bought on the black market for $48,000.

Disguise Kit

A large suitcase, generally filled with makeup and basic prosthetics, along with two wigs. Anything but the most rudimentary disguise can take from two to fifteen hours to properly construct, less if a trained crew is assisting the process. The more elaborate the disguise, the longer the process takes, as well as increasing the fragility of the disguise.

Rank 1: A makeup kit may allow for very basic disguises per G.M.'s discretion, but anything more overt than those slight changes requires a full disguise kit. Taking up about a full trunk, the disguise kit is generally too large to be taken on-site, unless special arrangements are made. This kit also comes complete with several basic sets of clothing, some of which may be specialized such as commercial uniforms or basic military fatigues. **Cost:** $400.

Rank 2: A full film special effects system has been set up to help create disguises. Latex skin, multiple wigs and prosthetics, as well as molds of various faces, both human and otherwise, all have been carefully set up to aid in this delicate process. This kit is considered stationary, as it needs to be set up first since it takes up the size of a large bathroom. It also contains a plethora of clothing, most of which is highly specialized for any specific situation. Dress uniforms for post-World War One France, gala ball gowns, and trendy fashion from the latest Milan shows, are all attainable. This kit adds a +10% to all disguise checks made in its vicinity. **Cost:** $1,600.

Rank 3: Complete with face-mask printing capability, some of which may be alien or high-tech gear, this room can create most any costume and disguise available, barring extreme physical or environmental changes, such as variable glowing from the target, magical auras and the like. Several of these items are highly-suspect, if not outright illegal. This kit adds a +20% to all disguise checks made at its location, as well as +20% to the quality of all disguise checks. **Cost:** Varies, and may require extensive resources and connections, but could be bought on the black market for $120,000.

Stage Magicians of Cascade
Regalia Red
– Archnemesis of the City of Cascade

Regalia Red is a city-wide menace in the dark city of Cascade. Elusive, inscrutable, deadly, and hell-bent on making the good citizens of the city suffer, Regalia Red has caused chaos in the streets on any number of occasions, urging people to resist authority and to tear down the comforts of society. A well-known anarchist, her targets are often the city government, as well as any large corporation that has its neck on the populace. Her attacks are generally flamboyant, humiliating, and deadly. More than one corporate executive or corrupt politician have found themselves hung from an invisible cord for all to see.

Most notably of late, Regalia Red had taken the city of Cascade hostage during Halloween Eve, a.k.a. Devil's Night, by somehow magicking away the Guz Holloman Bridge, the primary transportation route across the Sleego River. This combined with a power outage, left the city in dire straits as the Cascade City Police Departments were left scrambling to protect the city proper.

Regalia Red

Level 14 Stage Magician

Real Name: Unknown, though she has been active in Cascade for twelve years now.

Aliases: The Queen of Spades, The Heckler, The Matron of Puzzles.

Alignment: Anarchist.

Disposition: Ever a showwoman, Regalia Red enjoys combat as much as anything. Always quick to turn a phrase, she enjoys the rush of it all, taunting those she fights with a flair and a gesture that seems inhuman. She enjoys a great deal of costumes, intentionally invoking other figures of myth and legend as well as modern figures, especially ones such as the noted thief Carmen San Diego, or Peter Pan. Regalia Red secretly believes that civilization is on a knife's edge as it is, and that the only way for humanity to survive is to cast aside the weak, callow ways of large cities, and become more self-reliant. Heroes, to her, are a decent step towards her realized dream, but even they need to be challenged to ensure they're fit enough to survive.

Appearance: Nobody knows her true appearance, but her figure is highly noticeable. She is lithe, athletic and quite buxom for her size. Wearing a completely form-fitting outfit, the anarchist wears a swirling bodysuit that cloaks her face, though she tends to accessorize herself with extraneous gear such as overcoats, hats, or capes, as she delivers a flourish of taste and style as she does her best to steal the limelight.

Attributes: I.Q. 16, M.E. 15, M.A. 24, P.S. 17, P.P. 26, P.E. 16, P.B. 27, Spd 20.

S.D.C.: 65. **Hit Points:** 61.

Armor: Flexi-Steel Ultra-Lite Armor, A.R. 16, S.D.C. 200, weight 16 lbs (7.2 kg). +1 to strike when optics and targeting sights are engaged. Thermal vision. Night vision. -5% Prowl penalty. Made by Fabricators Inc.

Combat Bonuses: +4 Initiative.

Using Razor-Sharp Cards – 10 attacks a round, +14 to Strike, generally launching 4 cards at once for a total of 4D4+22 damage, (cards are high quality, +5 to damage each), +8 to Dodge, +4 to Dodge vs bullets, +5 to Auto-Dodge.

In Hand to Hand – 7 Attacks in a round. +7 to Strike, +8 to Entangle, +8 to Parry/Dodge.

Abilities: Sleight of Hand – 97%, Master of Escape – 98%, The Pledge (rank 1), The Turn, (rank 2), The Prestige (rank 2), Wealth (rank 2), Dodge Bullets (rank 1 AWMS ability), Blind Fighter (rank 1), Showstopper (rank 2), Multiple Shot (rank 1 AWMS ability), Cold at Heart (rank 1), Redirect Shot (rank 1 AWMS ability), Cumulative Strike (rank 1 AWMS ability), Antipodism (rank 2), Hidden Strike (rank 1 AWMS ability), Prowl, 98%, W.P. Targeting, W.P. Small Thrown Weapons, W.P. Sword, W.P. Staff, Perception 60%.

Typical Combat Actions: Set up an area via Showstopper to increase versatility. Use gear to distract or elude enemies, keep distance using grapple launcher, separate enemies to set up use of The Turn, and The Prestige for high damage with ranged attacks, and most importantly, never let them know why you're really there.

Equipment: Typically job specific. Favors metal playing cards with an extraordinarily powerful metal alloy, allowing for high damage per card. Also favors the standard tools of the trade. Has a vast array of backers and followers to help her instigate her crimes.

Bora the Elaborate

Level 2 Stage Magician

Name: Peggy Mathers.

Land of Origin: Cascade.

Alignment: Scrupulous.

Description: Bora enjoys masks as part of her motif. She has been known to dramatically change her outfits, but her go-to standard involves the classic professionalism that is known to stage magic. A full suit, with waistcoat, with an extra flair about the hips. She generally wears an eye mask, even beneath her full face masks, which differ between Tragedy and Comedy, among others.

History: Margaret Mathers took a shine to sleight of hand at a young age, enough that it helped her break out of her shell. It became her fallback, her go-to, and her passion. When her father lost his job, she started street performances. Within six months, she found herself caught on television, her act recorded to the internet. Since then, she's garnered a following, as well as backers who enjoy her politically-charged shows. With her swordcane, she's had to deal with thugs and toughs who disapprove of her platform.

Attributes: I.Q. 12, M.E. 14, M.A. 23, P.S. 15, P.P. 23, P.E. 17, P.B. 19, Spd 20.

S.D.C.: 38. **Hit Points:** 23.

Sleight of Hand: 81%

Master of Escape: 72%

Notable Skills: W.P. Sword, Cardsharp 70%, Prowl 55%, Imitate Voices 60%, Acrobatics, Ventriloquism 60%, Detect Concealment 45%.

Styles Taken:

Master of Blades – As per the Ancient Weapon Master Specialist (Sword Cane).
- Parry Projectile.
- Paralyzing Strike.
- Deadly Radius.

A Thousand Faces
- Quick Change Artist – Grants 3 costume changes a day.
- Impersonation – +10% Impersonation bonus to assume basic mundane identities.
- Face Masks – Always considered to be wearing a mask.

General
- Blind Fighter – Fights at half negatives in darkness.
- Expert Observer – +10% quality on Detect Concealment and Locate Secret Compartments checks.

Kelly Sharpe, Queen of Diamonds

Level 2 Stage Magician

Name: Natalie Burns.

Land of Origin: Detroit, Michigan, USA.

Alignment: Scrupulous.

Description: Kelly Sharpe favors a costume more like a carnival barker's outfit. She wears a stylized red and black suit and corset, along with a red top hat with black band. All aspects of the outfit are known to draw attention to her form.

History: Nat Burns really didn't want to come here. But when her younger sister, Kit, wanted to actually make something of her life by going to Sleego University for Pre-Med, Nat took on the role of primary income source for her sister. Three years later, she's been the ditzy blonde playing off of an aged magical act at one of the casinos in town. Longing for a life of greater purpose, she's taken to vigilante burglary of the thugs who haunt the nearby homes. Anything to pay the bills for her sister.

Attributes: I.Q. 13, M.E. 7, M.A. 20, P.S. 16, P.P. 21, P.E. 15, P.B. 24, Spd 18.

S.D.C.: 51. **Hit Points:** 24.
Sleight of Hand: 81%
Master of Escape: 72%
Notable Skills: Seduction 45%, Card Sharp 70%, Prowl 55%, Imitate Voices 60%, Gymnastics – Sense of Balance 66%, Track and Field, Acting 60%.
Styles Taken:

Cat Burglar
- Breaking and Entering – +10% to all breaking and entering skills needed against non-living targets.
- Master Burglar – +10% quality to Prowl rolls.

Mentalism
- Cold Read – three times a day.
- Knowing Your Audience – +10% to all social skills after assessing targets for 5 minutes.
- Hypnotic Suggestion – When the victim is unaware of your intentions, you may roll Psychology. If you succeed, you may implant a Hypnotic Suggestion as per the psionic power with a save vs Mentalism (14+), into his memory. You may not implant more than one Suggestion on a person at a time.
- Trance – When the victim is unaware of your intentions, you may roll Psychology. If you succeed, you may attempt to Trance Other as per the magic spell with a save vs Mentalism (14+).

General
- Expert Cardshark – +20% quality to Card Sharp rolls.
- Upgrade – Clinging Smoke Bombs – Smoke Bombs you prepare cling to those who were in its splash range.

In Conclusion

Together these abilities combine to form a character built around surprising foes and capitalizing on those brief moments. Cross-Training into Ancient Weapon Master Specialist, or further revitalized power categories, gives the Stage Magician a great edge in combat as well as increasing his natural affinity for juggling, and in a moment of surprise, can deliver a devastating combination. Whether they blend into the crowd, whispering hypnotic suggestions to targets on the street; throw down a smoke bomb, and lash out at the momentarily blinded; or befuddle and confuse those about him with his innovative offense and iconic gear, the Stage Magician has become a threat to the villains of the world. I expect to produce new and exciting variants of the Super Sleuth and Secret Operative as well, following this guideline.

Many thanks to my podcasting and gaming partners of over twenty years, The Guides to the Megaverse at collectiveidiocy.com, and to those adventuring souls in The Dark City of Cascade Facebook Group for their assistance and support.

Different Ways to Run a Campaign

Optional Rules and Modifiers for G.M.s

By Julius Rosenstein

What follows are some of the house rules and game mechanics I have experimented with over the years. I thought I'd share them with you. Whether you use some, or none of them, I hope you find this an interesting read.

Game Masters generally have a great deal of leeway when they design a campaign. Though they must abide by certain rules and stay within some specific parameters, there is no reason their campaigns should be churned out in a cookie cutter fashion. Often a little bit of advance planning and flexibility gives a role-playing campaign a distinctive feel. Tweaking the rules of any game system to your personal viewpoint and comfort level is commonplace and has always been encouraged by Kevin Siembieda and the rest of us at Palladium Books. Here are just a few ideas that have worked pretty well for me in the past.

Note: I have used some of these same ideas for **Heroes Unlimited™, Rifts®, Palladium Fantasy®,** and **Beyond the Supernatural™,** so they are not bound to just one genre or world setting. They can be used for various Palladium game worlds and variant rules.

Setting up the characters' levels

Some campaigns start with characters all at first level, others will start them higher so that they can take on and handle more powerful adversaries. The questions often become, "Do the characters all start at the same experience level? If not, how do you determine who starts at what level?"

There is always the basic method of starting everyone at first level or all at the same level. This is a very good idea when running *new players* – that is to say, players new to gaming or new to the system, as opposed to players familiar with the game rules but new to the Game Master. It is best not to overload newbies with too many new things to deal with. And if you have a bunch of new players, keep it simple and start them all off at first or second level.

However, when an experienced Game Master is running a game with experienced gamers, it might be more interesting to run a higher-powered campaign and characters with a range of experience. This may (or may not) call for higher level characters to maintain a game balance with the opposition they face. Of course, it is the Game Master's job to make sure the opposition is suitable for the player group regardless of level.

Or the G.M. may also simply tell the players they are all starting at level X, but here are some other options.

One way of determining experience levels is to simply decide which levels are available and have the players roll an appropriate die (i.e. if four levels are available, roll 1D4. If six are available, roll 1D6, etc.). This leaves determining the level of each player character up to Fate.

A method that I have used on occasion is to let the players choose from first to fourth level for their character. However, in order to prevent everyone from automatically opting for the highest level available, which can be fine, the method that I use to even things up is through experience points and how rapidly or slowly the characters advance from their starting point.

In this case, ALL the characters, no matter what level they start at, begin with *zero* actual experience points. This way, while the player characters gain the powers and abilities of 3rd or 4th level, they start at zero points and must earn reaching 5th level. From then on, all experience points awarded are divided by the level that the character started at. Thus, a 1st level character gets all (100%) of his experience, a 2nd level character gets half (50%), a 3rd level character gets 1/3 (33 1/3%), and a 4th level character keeps only a quarter (25%) of the points awarded.

Furthermore, the characters cannot advance in experience levels until they gain all the points they would normally have needed to reach their starting level. So a character who starts at 4th level does not get experience points without the penalty described above, until he reaches the minimum number to be 4th level. At that point, he gains experience without modifiers and advances in experience as normal. This may not necessarily seem like a great deal, but experience points add up faster than you might think, and make a difference over a long running campaign.

As an example, imagine that there are four characters who all enter the same O.C.C. Each character begins at a different level from first to fourth. Over a period of time, each of the characters earns 12,000 experience points (a nice, easily divisible figure). The first level character would keep all 12,000 points; the second level character would only get half (or 6,000) of those points; the third level character would only get a third (or 4,000) of those points; and the fourth level character would only get a quarter (or 3,000) of those points.

Let's assume that their particular O.C.C. requires 2,000 experience points to reach 2nd level, 4,000 to hit 3rd level, 8,000 to make 4th level, and 15,000 for 5th level. The 1st level character (who now has 12,000 points) is now at 4th level and more than halfway to 5th level (3,000 more points and he's made it). The character who begins at 2nd level (and has kept 6,000 experience points) is currently at 3rd level and is halfway to 4th level (2,000 more points are needed to reach the next level, but at the 50% penalty, it's actually 4,000 points that need to be earned). The character who starts at 3rd level is still at that level and has just earned the 4,000 points that he actually needs for his current level. All points after this are applied toward reaching 4th level (he needs 4,000 more points to reach that level; however, because of the penalty for starting at 3rd level, the points earned will have to be tripled, requiring a total of 12,000 needed). Finally, the character who started at 4th level is not even halfway to the true amount of experience that the character would normally need for his current level (he needs 5,000 more points which will have to be multiplied by four for a total of 20,000 just to finally reach his current level. Any experience points beyond this will go toward earning the advance to 5th level).

Game Masters who feel that this method causes too great a disparity in the characters may opt to eliminate dividing the experience points by the character's initial level once that character has amassed the sufficient amount of experience points that are normally required to reach that particular level. However, it should be reminded that these characters began with advantages (due to their higher level) over their comrades and having the other characters (who started at lower levels) getting their chance to shine is just fair play.

Getting the group together

Once the players have their characters all set and the campaign is ready to begin, the Game Master now has to introduce the characters into the campaign setting. Although some campaigns lend themselves toward bringing the characters into a campaign at different times and places, most campaigns start by bringing in all (or most) of the characters together from the start. This is ideal as it is no fun for any player to be sitting on his hands waiting to be introduced while other players are having fun with their characters.

One decision of the Game Master involves the familiarity of the characters with one another, i.e., do the characters know each other or not? Some Game Masters make it simple and declare that the characters already know each other and are friends. Other Game Masters have the characters all be total strangers who happen to meet and share the same goals (saving lives, making money, stopping the evil so and so, etc.). They learn about each other through interaction via role-playing during the campaign itself. I know Kevin Siembieda likes to have players with a common goal meet and learn about each other through gaming interaction. **Note**: A group of strangers (i.e. the different player characters) meeting for the first time at a bar has been used so often, it has pretty much become a standard to some G.M.s and a cliche to others, but if it works, it works. The point is, get everyone together as quickly as you can so the game can get going. Likewise, players should cooperate in this matter, and agree to have their characters work together even if they have their doubts or suspicions about some of their new teammates. This can be easier in a superhero game if the characters have a reputation.

There are benefits and disadvantages to both of these methods. However, depending upon the nature of the campaign and the players, I have often selected a third option: Have some of the characters know each other, either by choice or by chance.

If familiarity is being allowed by choice, I look at the backgrounds of the various characters. O.C.C.s are very important, since characters who in the same line of work often tend to know one another – either as friends and colleagues or as competitors and rivals. In campaigns where there is more than one species, race and culture can also play an important part since many beings prefer to associate with others like themselves and gravitate toward people of similar background and culture. Other factors such as social status, where the respective characters live, work, play, study, and even relax, may help to determine which characters may have met each other prior to the start of the campaign.

On the other hand, if their previous history is left up to chance, then I resolve this by having all of the players roll a D6 for each character and then comparing their roll with the rolls of the other characters. The differences will range from zero to five, and the closer any two rolls are to one another, the better those characters will know each other.

Initial Familiarity (roll 1D6 and compare the difference, modifying when necessary):

Difference of Zero (same number rolled for both characters): The characters know each other quite well and have worked together on at least one mission, if not several. These characters may each consider the other a friend and teammate, or dislike each other or dislike the way the other conducts himself (players' choice).

Difference of One (1 & 2, 2 & 3, etc.): The characters have either worked briefly with each other but not gone on a mission together, or they have not adventured together but still know each other fairly well. They are probably more like coworkers than friends.

Difference of Two (1 & 3, 2 & 4, etc.): The characters are either casual acquaintances or they have met only briefly, in passing. Their impression of one another may be positive or negative (players' choice).

Difference of Three (1 & 4, 2 & 5, 3 & 6): The characters only know each other vaguely by reputation, or have seen each other from a distance, but have never actually met. Their impression of one another may be positive, negative or indifferent (players' choice).

Difference of Four (1 & 5, 2 & 6): The characters have heard of each other only briefly, in passing, but have never met and don't really have any opinion about one another.

Difference of Five (1 & 6): The characters are total strangers who have never met, seen, or even heard of each other.

Exceptions to the Rule: Characters who are brand new are automatically unfamiliar with everybody else. New characters who join the campaign later may know some of the more established characters by reputation (differences of 0 or 1 are dropped to a result of 2).

Skills Unlimited (more or less)

More house rules

As it stands, nearly all of the non-combative skills (i.e. everything except Weapon Proficiencies and Hand to Hand Combat skills) of the Palladium Megaversal System are based on percentiles with a cap of 98%. Normally this means that someone attempting to use a skill must roll percentile against their skill. A roll under their skill level means a success, a roll above the skill level means a failure. Of course, there is always the possibility of applying situational modifiers which may either increase or decrease the character's chance of success.

However, to add further variety in my campaigns, I have tweaked the skill system a little more in three ways: **A)** Allowing certain characters to go beyond the 98% cap. **B)** Permitting players to use prerequisites as backup skills. And **C)** in certain cases, allowing players to create skills that are not listed in the official rule books.

A) Beyond 98%. Normally, a master of a particular skill (i.e. someone with a skill of 98%) has only a 2% chance of failing when they attempt to use that skill. However, such is not always the case thanks to modifiers. Thus, a jet pilot with a skill of 98% attempting to fly a foreign jet plane – one he has never flown before and whose controls are in a foreign language and script – might be assigned a skill penalty of -50%, leaving him with only a 48% chance to successfully fly this plane. On the other hand, without the 98% limit, a pilot who has attained a skill of 130% can take the same penalty and still have a success rate of 80%. **Note:** Even without penalties or modifiers, a Natural roll of 99% or 00% still fails, even if the character's skill is greater than 100%.

In addition to the sheer superior skill the character has attained, having a skill higher than 98% carries another advantage in my campaigns. These incredibly high skilled characters can become *innovators* in those skills. Essentially, having a 98% means the character knows all there basically is to know (i.e. common knowledge) concerning a specific skill, and having a score above 100% means the character is capable of progressing beyond the sum of knowledge normally attributed to that skill and, through his unique insight, can add more knowledge to the currently known pool.

In other words, a 98% skill master "knows the book" by heart; a 100+% skill master has "written the book." A character's chance of having a breakthrough equals his skill score -100, divided by 10 (rounded up). Thus, for example, a character with a score of 130% will have a 3% chance (130 - 100 = 30, divided by 10 = 3%) of having a breakthrough in using that particular skill, such as a work-around, a jury-rig modification, a way to successfully perform an unlikely maneuver, etc., that someone with lesser skill is unlikely to recognize. Note that these flashes only occur on a Natural roll. If the roll is in the insight range due to modifiers, the flash of genius does not occur. It is just a normal success, even if it is a critical success.

In order to prevent a ridiculous number of "skill geniuses," I have limited these *skill masteries* to characters who *begin* the campaign with that particular skill. My rationale is that if someone has worked toward becoming a particular occupation or mastering a particular skill, whether it be bio-engineering or playing a guitar, from their childhood, they will be more likely to master it than a latecomer.

As a contrived example, three boyhood friends decide on different paths for their lives: a rock star, a carpenter, and a sailor. They each plan to become masters in their respective fields and also make a pact to train each other in their various skills. Conceivably, each of the trio could exceed 98% in certain skills that are inherent to their chosen dream occupations (i.e. the rock star in Play Musical Instrument, Sing, and Perform; the carpenter in Carpentry, General Repair and Maintenance, and Jury-Rig; and the sailor in Pilot: Boat (sail and/or motored), and Swimming. However, despite their best efforts – and even with personal coaching from the skill masters – their friends would be unable to top 98% in skills that are not intrinsically applicable to their own chosen professions.

B) Prerequisites as backup skills: Some skills serve as prerequisites. In other words, before certain skills can be taken, other skills are required to be known first. For example, in order to take the skill *Medical Doctor*, a character first has to have the skills of Biology, Pathology, Chemistry, Mathematics (Basic or Advanced), and Literacy. In some cases, a prerequisite skill itself requires a previous skill(s). For example, the Weapons Engineer skill has only one prerequisite skill listed – Mechanical Engineering. However, Mechanical Engineering itself has three prerequisites: Basic Electronics, Mathematics (Basic or Advanced), and Literacy.

Oddly, other skills which seem as if they should have prerequisites do not. For examples, Aircraft Mechanics, Automotive Mechanics, Bioware Mechanics, and Mechanical Engineer do NOT require the skill of Basic Mechanics. Although Chemistry: Analytical requires the basic Chemistry skill, the Chemistry: Pharmaceutical skill does not.

For complex or uncommon skills, I will sometimes assign a prerequisite(s) skill. However, this is a matter of personal preference as I do not want to make the obtaining of advanced skills in my campaigns too easy. Originally, this tactic did have the drawback of causing some of my players (the power-mongers among them) to complain that this was making obtaining a range of skills too difficult.

To compensate for this, I decided to let the prerequisite skills serve as backup skills. For game purposes, I consider the prerequisite skill as the wider-ranging, and more comprehensive, but ultimately, more superficial skill while the more advanced skill is narrower in focus but more specific in what it does cover. Thus, if the character fails when rolling for the advanced skill, he can roll again using his prerequisite skill with a penalty (described below).

For example, a character with Chemistry: Analytical needs to analyze an unusual chemical compound. Even if he fails his Chemistry: Analytical skill, he can roll again, this time under the Basic Chemistry skill, but at -20%. Thus, although this policy limits the sheer number of skills the character may have, it allows him to generally be more successful at the skills he does possess. The base penalty for a second-chance roll using a prerequisite skill is -20%. However, the G.M. may increase this penalty up to –50% based on the level of difficulty, harsh conditions, stress level, or the strange nature of working on something extremely alien or unknown to him.

C) Creating new skills that are not listed in the official rule book: Although it is not common, another thing that I sometimes permit is for players to design *personal skills*. This is NEVER anything major and is only allowed *if* the player has a specific concept in mind that I feel will enhance his or her role-playing and the player is willing to put in the time and work to develop that skill. I have seen personal skills in my own campaigns that allowed different characters to become an expert in detailing motor vehicles (vans, SUVs, and sports cars), a gourmet on ice cream (no other foods, only ice cream), and an authority on 18th Century French authors.

What to do when a character leaves the campaign

Characters sometime leave a campaign, usually because the player running them can no longer continue to do so. School, work, children, and many other demands and pressures from life can cause a player to drop out of a game on a temporary or permanent basis. Some gamers are willing to leave their characters in the hands of a fellow player, or with the Game Master to use as an NPC (Non-Player Character). Other players won't like the idea, preferring to remove a favorite character from the game to prevent anything adverse happening to the character. (Indeed, anyone given charge of someone else's character should take great care to, a) play in character, and b) make sure the character does not get destroyed while in their care.)

The simplest solution is for the player and Game Master to work together to find a plausible reason for that character to leave the campaign. He could be reassigned to a different mission, different department or even a different country, world or dimension! Or the character may go off to follow a different lead and take a back seat or desk job, where he or she can function in a secondary NPC capacity. In other cases, the player may elect to literally retire his character, or go undercover or into witness protection (or equivalent). If the player would like to see his character go out in a blaze of glory and die (rare, but I've seen it happen), the G.M. should try to accommodate him/her unless the request is disruptive to the game. (Players, be reasonable and considerate of the G.M., the other players and the campaign.) In short, use whatever story device works best without killing the character (unless that's what the payer really wants). The kinds of things you've seen a hundred times when a regular character leaves a TV show. And whenever possible, leave things open so that the player and character can return in the future if life circumstance allows it.

I have found the best reason for a character to leave his or her comrades behind is to follow a new course. For example, a personal quest may arise (e.g. rescue a friend or loved one, find and/or destroy a magical artifact, personal discovery, etc.), or he may achieve or acquire a position (e.g. inherit a fiefdom, gain a promotion, become the hero/protector of a particular town, city, world, and so on). This way, the character survives and can be brought back if things change for the player, and the goals and plans of the main group also remain intact.

A possible deterrent to this is the concern of starting over. Some players (and G.M.s) may still cling to the outmoded idea of maintaining a specific character at all costs.

Similarly, a player may simply want to retire his current character and bring in a new character. Someone fresh and different. I always allow this. Years ago, in the early days of role-playing, there was an attitude of hanging on to a certain character, no matter what. This idea was that once a character was rolled up, only two things could take this character out of a campaign: The character could get killed (with no chance of resurrection), or the campaign itself would end. This meant that sometimes the character would have to act out of character in order to remain in the game. For example, the classic fairy tale reward of "the hand of the princess in marriage and half the kingdom" would have to be refused by someone who wants to keep adventuring with his group, even if it would make more sense for the character to take the reward and leave the group. When something like that happens, I let the character follow the course the player thinks is best, and let the player introduce a new character to play.

Here's an example: In a campaign that took place aboard a starship, one player was promoted up through the ranks to become the Executive Officer (i.e. the second in command) of the ship. Then, the character did something else notable and was rewarded further. For his reward, he could opt either for a promotion to Captain or have the High Command owe him a favor; a favor to be called in if he ever wanted to do so.

Since the Captain of his ship was a fellow player character, he realized that a promotion would mean that his character would have to be transferred off his ship and into his own command elsewhere, effectively ending that particular character in our ongoing campaign. However, the player decided that his character would take the promotion and essentially had his character promoted right out of the game. He simply brought in a new character and continued in the campaign playing a new guy.

This brings us back to the starting level of a player character. For some Game Masters, if a character leaves the campaign, it often means the player's new character starts at first level. To many players, after investing a lot of time and effort into building a character up to a decent level, having to start over seems like more of a punishment than a new beginning, especially if he or she retired the character because it made sense to the story. A player should not be punished for excellent *role-playing*.

A solution that has worked for me and several of my friends, is to take the amassed experience points (including those from the most recent adventure) of the retired character and apply them to the player's new one.

For example, a character who already has 5,000 experience points goes on an adventure and does things that should gain him another 300 points. However, he also encounters or does something (such as agreeing to go on a quest) that does not kill him but sends the character out of the campaign. To stay in the main campaign, the player must roll up a new character. Instead of that new character starting at first level with zero experience points, the new character starts with same experience as the character that was retired. In this example, that would be 5,300 points of experience.

Admittedly, this is a procedure in which the determining factors are subjective. If a player is simply tired of running a character or loses a character due to playing foolishly, then (if I am the G.M.) I will usually make his new character start from scratch, i.e. level one and zero experience points. However, if the reason for retiring the character is a valid one, or if the character dies in an exceptional manner – generally involving either good role-playing with some bad luck from bad die rolls, and/or self-sacrifice – then I allow the new character to either have the same experience points as the previous character if he had remained in the campaign, or start at the same level with the base experience points for that level. I know Kevin Siembieda does the same thing.

Finishing the Campaign – Character Closure

As enjoyable as some role-playing campaigns can be, eventually a campaign must come to an end. Something that not all Game Masters necessarily consider or are prepared to handle. It's okay. Follow the story arc to a satisfying conclusion and if you can, make the final fate of the characters be as satisfying as possible.

My feeling is that this is somewhat akin to a television series. You want to avoid a "final season" that ends on a cliffhanger, because it ends with the ultimate fates of the characters still not completely resolved. The players are left in the lurch as to what will ultimately befall the characters that they have come to know and love.

Personally, when a group of people play in one of my campaigns for awhile, I feel that they are entitled to see how their characters finally end up. Thus, I try to make sure that my gamers not only get a final opportunity for their characters to act within the game itself, but that they also receive a final recap of what fates ultimately befall each of them, if they so desire. Depending upon the actions of the characters, this could entail either a fair amount of extrapolating on the part of the G.M. or just rubber stamping the character.

This final extrapolation is omitted if the player(s) would prefer to leave their ultimate fate open and unknown. The main reason that this may occur is if they want to use the character at some later date in another campaign, provided the Game Master will permit this.

As an example, there was a character who, in one **Palladium Fantasy®** campaign, began as a freelance adventurer and eventually fell in love with a (NPC) Bizantine princess. In the extrapolation, the pair married, raised several children, the princess eventually became queen, and the (now former) adventurer became the Prince Consort of Bizantium.

Years later in real time, when the Game Master decided to run a new campaign, it was set some 30 years later and the adventurer, who was now middle-aged, was briefly in the campaign as an elder statesman to pass the torch to a younger generation of heroes.

In another example, for a **Beyond the Supernatural™** campaign that recently ended (after it ran for more than three years), during the "final session" I gave the players the opportunity to decide for themselves how they wanted their characters to end. Whether they wanted to receive their "happy endings," or if they felt that their character would continue on an undetermined path of adventure.

One of them, whose character was a doctor, decided to forgo active adventuring in favor of becoming a support character. She would leave the hospital where she worked and start her own private practice where she would tend to "special" patients, thus still helping the cause but now as a semi-NPC, if there was ever a sequel campaign.

Another player decided to have his character sell all of his non-portable possessions, and (along with his NPC girlfriend) go on an extended journey, which would eventually take him somewhere that his former comrades and friends would never be able to track him. Eventually, his character would get his well-deserved retirement.

The other three players decided that they would keep their characters and either remain active as secret protectors within the city (off-campaign, as it were) or simply retire from adventuring and live in the city they helped defend so many times. Thus, if a new campaign were ever to pick up where this one ended, not only do these players have established characters all ready to step in and resume their careers as heroes, but if the G.M. so chooses, the time elapsed between campaigns (i.e. where this campaign ended and the next one begins) can be applied toward setting up the background for the new campaign.

In summary, what I'm trying to say is, ideas that may be innovative and entertaining the first time they are used can become dull and boring with repetition. As good as the rules for the Palladium Megaversal Game System are, they are not carved in stone. That's true of any game system. Kevin Siembieda, the creator of the game worlds mentioned in this article, is a master of improvisation, and one of the most flexible, inventive Game Masters I have ever gamed with. So was Erick Wujcik, though Erick had his own unique style and approach to Game Mastering. Every G.M. does. Being open and flexible, however, was a common trait. One I share with them, as do many of the Game Masters I know and like to game with.

Remember, give the players options and some latitude. Follow some of their cues and ideas, and never be afraid to improvise or modify rules to make a good idea work in your game. Often, when individual players are allowed to take their characters beyond the norm, it can add to the enjoyment of the campaign, for the players and Game Masters alike.